MENTAL MECHANISMS

Mental Mechanisms

THE MENTAL MECHANISMS
REPRESSION
SUBLIMATION
IDENTIFICATION
INVERSION
COMPENSATION
RESTITUTION

Henry P. Laughlin

Practicing Psychiatrist in Bethesda-Chevy
Chase, Maryland; Associate Clinical Pro-
fessor of Psychiatry, George Washington
University School of Medicine, Washington,
D.C.; Head, Division of Psychiatry, Subur-
ban Hospital, Bethesda, Maryland.

WASHINGTON
BUTTERWORTHS
1963

U.S.A.:   BUTTERWORTH INC.
               WASHINGTON, D.C.: 7235 Wisconsin Avenue, 14

ENGLAND: BUTTERWORTH & CO. (PUBLISHERS) LTD.
               LONDON: 88 Kingsway, W.C.2

AFRICA: BUTTERWORTH & CO. (AFRICA) LTD.
               DURBAN: 33/35 Beach Grove

AUSTRALIA: BUTTERWORTH & CO. (AUSTRALIA) LTD.
               SYDNEY: 6/8 O'Connell Street
               MELBOURNE: 430 Bourke Street
               BRISBANE: 240 Queen Street

CANADA: BUTTERWORTH & CO. (CANADA) LTD.
               TORONTO: 1367 Danforth Avenue, 6

NEW ZEALAND: BUTTERWORTH & CO. (NEW ZEALAND) LTD.
               WELLINGTON: 49/51 Ballance Street
               AUCKLAND: 35 High Street

BF175
L3x

Library of Congress Catalogue Card No: 63-21088

PRINTED IN THE UNITED STATES OF AMERICA
BY PORT CITY PRESS, INC., BALTIMORE, MARYLAND

CONTENTS

v

DEDICATION

Fondly and fraternally dedicated to my friends and colleagues from . . .

Hagerstown, Md., Public Schools

Ursinus College, Johns Hopkins University, and Temple University School of Medicine

Theta Upsilon of *Phi Chi*

The Babcock Surgical Society

Saint Elizabeths Hospital

The U.S. Navy Medical Corps, and the Philadelphia Post Graduate Training Program in Psychiatry

The American Psychiatric Association

Suburban, George Washington University, D.C. General, and Sibley Hospital Staffs

The George Washington University Medical School Graduates, Faculty, and Department of Psychiatry

The Washington Psychiatric Society

Various host nations, universities, institutions, and societies

U.S.A. S.G.O.-Walter Reed A.M.C. Graduate Training Program in Psychiatry

The American Board of Psychiatry and Neurology Examiners and Assistant Examiners

The Montgomery County, Maryland, Medical Society

The Washington-Baltimore Psychoanalytic Institute

The Royal Medico-Psychological Association

H.E.W.-U.S.P.H.S. Research Project in Executive Development

The Modern Founders of the A.P.A.

United States Agencies: P.S.B.; E.C.A., M.S.A., I.C.A., AID.; and D.L.F.

The Medical Arts Society of Greater Washington

The Academy of Psychoanalysis

The National Psychiatric Endowment Fund

American Association of Psychoanalytic Physicians

House of Delegates, Committees and Council; The Medical and Chirurgical Faculty of the State of Maryland

The Eastern Psychoanalytic Association

Washington Medical and Surgical Society

The College of American Psychiatrists

. . . Butterworth Inc., publishers, have been instructed to pay any and all royalties from Mental Mechanisms, *and from the forthcoming new edition of* The Neuroses *directly and proportionally to certain of the above organizations, which elect to initiate therewith special Award Funds for achievement and service.*

vi

FOREWORD

This modest volume offers an introduction to the mental mechanisms, with some observations concerning six important members of the group. It is an outgrowth of my experience clinically, in teaching, and in assisting with the examinations of The American Board of Psychiatry and Neurology.

Accordingly, the Candidate for Boards has been constantly kept in mind, as has the Resident and Student. Dynamisms being so basic and universal in human psychology however, it might be hoped that this material could have some wider interest for my psychiatric colleagues, and in the behavioral sciences more generally.

Acknowledgment is gratefully made to the friends and students who provided several of the case histories, to typist Lenore McComas, the Bulletin of the Montgomery County Medical Society as publisher of some preliminary material, Jack K. Burgess and Linton M. Vandiver of Butterworths, research assistant Hella Freud Bernays, a patient family, and to those friends and associates who have encouraged these efforts in writing, since long prior to the publication of the first edition of *The Neuroses,* in 1956.

It is hoped to follow this "Blue Book" on the mental mechanisms by a similar and continuing "Red Book" on additional mechanisms.

Seven Springs Farm,
Mt. Airy, Maryland
August 31, 1963

Henry P. Laughlin, M.D.

CHAPTER 1

THE MENTAL MECHANISMS

. . . bases of human behavior . . .

1. INTRODUCTION

A. UNIVERSALITY OF THE MENTAL MECHANISMS

Through scientific observation, study, and research into human behavior over the last several decades, a group of internal, psychologic processes has become widely recognized. They are of great importance and their use is widespread. It is not enough, however, to state that we human beings use these processes widely; their use is universal. Their employment, which is largely outside of conscious awareness, is indispensable to human adjustment.

Every observant student of human psychology encounters these major and vital processes frequently, and it is generally not too

1

difficult to recognize something of their operation. They are our intrapsychic mechanisms of defense. They are most familiarly and widely known as the *mental mechanisms.*

B. INTRAPSYCHIC DEFENSIVE OPERATIONS

(1) The resolution of internal conflict

In essence, the mental mechanisms are defensive operations. They develop within the psyche for the general purposes of helping the individual to improve his adaptation to life, and to bolster his psychologic defenses.

Accordingly, the human organism "makes use" of these mechanisms in its unconscious endeavors to resolve its emotional conflicts. The individual "seeks" in particular to resolve those conflicts which are intrapsychic. These are internal conflicts taking place between the major parts of one's personality as, for example, the conflict between an urge or drive and one's conscience, which forbids its gratification.

Important conflicts also arise between a major aspect of one's personality and some demand or requirement of his environment. In these the desires and needs of the individual come into conflict with the restrictions and limitations of society.

(2) Ego defenses against psychic pain and anxiety

The aim and intent of a mental mechanism is the avoidance of psychic discomfort and pain. Its operation is an important function of that major part of one's personality which is called the ego. Mental mechanisms are accordingly also called *ego defenses.*

Thus we learn that various mental mechanisms may be "employed" by people as part of their individual defensive operations. Conflict solution or resolution is a major goal. The prevention or allaying of ensuing anxiety is sought.

There are a score or more of these mechanisms which are reasonably distinct and which we have learned to identify with considerable accuracy. Currently their delineation has substantial professional agreement. Among the more familiar ones are such widely employed ego defenses as Rationalization, Compensation, and Identification. Another dozen are commonly seen, and nearly forty major and minor ones may be delineated.

2

C. RESPONSES TO DANGER

(1) Response to internal psychic danger

It is helpful to regard the mental mechanisms as *psychologic* responses to a more *internal* kind of threat or danger. This is in analogous fashion to the many *physical* kinds of preparation for "fight" or "flight" which may occur in response to a more strictly physical and external threat or danger. These latter *physical* and *physiologic* changes take place particularly in response to the kinds of danger which are primarily *external*, or extrapsychic. The accompanying emotional response is *fear*.

In turn, the mental mechanisms are the *psychologic* endeavors by which one unconsciously attempts to cope with danger which is primarily internal, or intrapsychic. This kind of threat or danger is not in conscious awareness. The accompanying emotional response is *anxiety*. In other words external dangers may be met by a physical and actual, fight or flight. Internal dangers are met by a psychic fight or flight. Mental mechanisms are called into play as part of the fight or flight in response to internal dangers.

(2) The sequence of responses: anxiety, dynamism, hypertrophy or failure, leading to emotional illness

Man seeks to avoid anxiety in every possible way. One major consequence of this avoidance is the employment of mental mechanisms. Their hypertrophy or failure leads to pathology. This is a central formulation in today's dynamic concept of the origin of the emotional illnesses, whether these illnesses are neuroses or functional psychoses.

Internal danger arises from serious emotional conflicts. The mental mechanisms are attempts at reaching acceptable solutions and compromises when the individual is faced with serious emotional conflicts; ones which would otherwise prove intolerable. As attempted defenses against anxiety, they provide a more acceptable kind of internal compromise or resolution. As we shall soon see, the overall result may be very self-defeating to the individual concerned. Nevertheless, they are most vital to him and are likely in turn to be held on to grimly, and to be defended most vigorously.

(3) Differing defensive operations in response to similar threats

At this point, then, let us consider two brief and simplified initial clinical examples in which the major mental mechanisms

3

of Rationalization (*Case 1*) and Projection (*Case 2*) were defensively employed. These cases help illustrate certain points already made and others to come. They also point out how the same kind of threat can result in two completely different types of defensive operations.

Case 1

Rationalization as a Defense in Promotion-Failure

A 44-year-old federal executive had been passed over when a position of higher echelon became vacant. A person outside of the organization was brought in to take the assignment. This was the third or fourth such event over the preceding five or so years. He had seemingly reached his limit of advancement. This had appeared increasingly apparent to him and to his colleagues.

Did he appear discouraged or disappointed? He did not. In this area of living he seemed unconcerned and even resigned. To a colleague who had known him over the years this was puzzling. Earlier he was most energetic and ambitious and had a considerable interest in professional advancement.

Not long after the event of his having again failed to be promoted, circumstances which were largely familial led him to seek psychotherapy. It gradually became clear over several months of treatment that his seeming lack of concern about his non-promotion was a protective cover. To the contrary, his real level of desire for promotion had been so very strong, that his failure to achieve promotion had become absolutely intolerable to him personally. The only way that he could tolerate life under these circumstances was to adopt the attitude and belief that he didn't care. On a conscious level he thoroughly believed this.

This was a vital defensive process. He had "sold himself" on the belief that he was uninterested in getting ahead. Promotion was unimportant to him! This even provided a kind of superior-to-others feeling for him. He would defend his views most vigorously if they were challenged. Consciously he was unaware of all this. He had employed the mental mechanism of *Rationalization*. Its use had been successful. By his Rationalization he had submerged his intolerable hurt, and exchanged for it on the level of consciousness, an attitude of non-concern. With the latter he was less vulnerable to hurt. Further, by adoption of the rationalized attitude he avoided recognition of some painful things about himself. These included certain quite specific handicapping personality traits. These had helped contribute to his failure to be selected for promotion to a more responsible position.

4

In the course of therapy this particular rationalization, among several other noteworthy ones, gradually crumbled. Eventually they came into conscious awareness. This man became able to accept his real drive for success, to modify it in line with his genuine potential. As he gained ability to see himself more clearly, he also became able to recognize and to constructively modify some of the factors which had accounted for his professional promotion-failure in the first place. Eighteen months after beginning treatment he was promoted to a much-desired position. A second promotion was secured after about three additional years.

A second example offers some interesting similarities and contrasts. The precipitating difficulty in the following case is similar, but the path taken by this patient's intrapsychic operations was quite different in character. So also was the ultimate outcome.

Case 2
Projection as a Defense in Promotion-Failure

A 52-year-old captain in the U.S. Navy had been passed over seven times for promotion to rear admiral. As time progressed, he had become increasingly bitter toward those who had failed to select him. It had become more and more difficult for him to maintain his self-esteem in the face of the repeated failures to advance in his professional career. His endeavor had gradually become one of attempting to avoid any conscious recognition of possible personal short-comings, which could have contributed to his difficulty. He also could not face the recognition that he was not held in great esteem by fellow service officers generally.

He began early and very gradually, but with increasing weight and certainty, to attribute his failure to a special few; to bias against him. He became convinced that several senior officers "had it in for him." He believed that he had been singled out for bad treatment.

This feeling slowly became more pervasive. It progressed inexorably to include his colleagues. As a consequence, his own attitudes and reactions became more antagonistic and suspicious. In a self-defeating kind of vicious circle this in turn had provided still more basis for his continued non-selection. This officer was a rather hostile person who came more and more to impute to others his own unfriendliness, distrust, and hatred. The mental mechanism which was operating here was *Projection*.

This mental mechanism was the defensive process developed to help conceal from his conscious recognition his own shortcomings, failures, and hostility. Such recognition was consciously intolerable. Instead of "I hate you," it had become to him "You hate me, and try to do me injury." Instead of "Since I haven't been selected for promotion, there must be ways in which I don't measure up," it had become, "I am not selected for promotion, not because of things about me, but because I have enemies who are plotting against me. . . . It's not my doing, I have no responsibility in it. I'm the victim of unfair treatment." These reactions on the part of others he did not imagine or merely believe. To him they were very realistically experienced, and he reacted to them accordingly.*

This is a very pathologic reaction. Yet we can still see how the initiation of this mental mechanism was in attempted defense. Tragically, as we can observe, it helped to ensure his permanent failure to be promoted. The net results were most self defeating.

Such an iron-clad system is most difficult to break into therapeutically. In this instance the only possible course proved to be his retirement. While this helped to solve the Navy's problem—administratively—it did not help solve the hopeless dilemma of this officer and his desperately handicapping pattern of intrapsychic defense operations. His pattern of Projection was deeply rooted and his retirement had no beneficial or therapeutic effect upon it. If anything, the convictions already held were strengthened further.

(4) The seeking of an acceptable solution, the resolution of conflict or emotional compromise

In each of the foregoing cases the intent of the unconscious endeavor was defensive. Resolution of serious emotional conflict was sought. Both these patients had found conscious recognition of certain facts about themselves and their adjustment to life intolerable. The mental mechanisms were elicited by the resulting serious emotional conflict. Their aim or goal was to avoid psychic pain. Conscious recognition would be too threatening. The ego is defended against this by its own individual type of ego defense. The danger was psychologic and essentially internal. The mental

---

* This illustrates in succinct fashion the important distinction between *subjective* reality, and *objective* reality. What the patient perceives is realistic to him, but subjectively so. What the detached and independent observer is likely to see is different. It is also realistic, but objectively so; a tremendous asset to accuracy.

mechanisms employed were part of the psyche's efforts to reach a more acceptable kind of solution or compromise.

In these cases the defensive operation resulted in handicap and limitation in the first instance, and serious emotional illness in the second. Not all usages of mental mechanisms have such inimical consequences by any means. It is well, however, for us to clearly recognize that such potentials exist. It is also well for us to clearly recognize their vital position in the psychogenesis of emotional illness. These cases provide apt illustration of the central import of mechanisms. They also help point out the necessity for our learning everything we can about them if we are to secure any real understanding of the development and initiation of the emotional illnesses.

D. AUTOMATIC AND UNCONSCIOUS PROCESSES

It is important to stress not only that mental mechanisms are utilized by everyone, but also that they are employed automatically and outside of conscious awareness. Thus it is far easier for an outside observer to recognize them than the person himself. The particular ones which may be identified or uncovered in the psychologic operations of a given person are strictly individual as to type, combination, and relative prominence.

A mental mechanism may develop to cope with some fairly narrow segment of living. On the other hand it may also become so important as to become the major factor in one's adjustment to life; or even so pervasive as to practically constitute a way of life in itself. To whatever extent this takes place, its development and operation are automatic and unconscious. Deliberate effort may be undertaken in full conscious awareness, of an identical aim and name. When this is true, however, the process is not a genuine mental mechanism. These points are perhaps clearer in the light of the preceding case illustrations.

This is an introduction to the study of mental mechanisms. Every student of human behavior should be vitally interested in these internal psychologic operations; what they are, how they arise, the forms they take, and some of the possible consequences of their operation.

E. UNDERSTANDING VITAL IN PSYCHOTHERAPY

It becomes clearly apparent, therefore, that familiarity with mental mechanisms is a basic requisite for anyone working closely

7

with those who suffer from mental and emotional illnesses. This is particularly true for anyone who is interested in doing psychotherapy.

A most important goal in modern psychotherapy is the increase of the self-understanding of the patient. An increase of insight is sought. The patient needs to learn more about what makes him "tick" as a person. This means that, with the help of the therapist, the patient undertakes the working out of the important "whys" and "hows" of his psychologic defenses. Inevitably to varying degrees, this will most likely include a fair amount of *de*repression; the bringing of previously unconscious material into conscious awareness. Following its recall to consciousness, its existence must be accepted; it must be reconciled with material which is already conscious, and it must be studied and understood. Not infrequently in the course of all this, it will undergo some degree of modification as to its emotional import. This can be most beneficial to the patient.

Successful treatment will inevitably result in greater understanding by both patient and physician of the intrapsychic defense operations; the mental mechanisms. The more knowledge the therapist already possesses concerning the general principles of their operation, the better the chances are for therapeutic success, and the speedier will be the progress of therapy. While patients with specific symptoms, or those having handicapping personality traits, are usually thought of in connection with therapy, it should be carefully noted that such a therapeutic process of self study and self education has an almost universal potential for usefulness. Psychotherapy may be regarded as an educational process; one of considerable depth.

2. DYNAMIC PSYCHIATRY

Modern conceptions regard human personality and its various emotional and mental components as a dynamic whole. The study of *dynamic* psychiatry focuses the direction of interest upon those factors in human behavior that are active, laden with energy, and ever changing. This is in distinction to an older, more static type of *descriptive* psychiatry, in which the emphasis of study was largely directed toward clinical patterns, symptoms, life history, and classification.

The word "dynamic" used as an adjective, indicates energy potential, constant change, shifting emphasis, mutual interaction, growth, evolution, and development. In psychiatry, therefore, dynamic principles are those which are compelling, driving, filled with energy, and forceful. They inevitably produce change and evolution. From an emotional health standpoint such changes may be progressive and healthful. They can also be regressive.

(1) Dynamisms

The mental mechanisms, their development and sequellae, are an inseparable and major part of dynamic psychiatry. They are dynamic in, and of themselves, as well as making personality adjustment and integration into a dynamic process. Accordingly, the label of "dynamism" as an alternative and interchangeable term with mental mechanism is quite appropriate for modern dynamic psychiatry.

As with the concept and term of ego defense as noted earlier, the term "dynamism" likewise offers certain advantages. Some people therefore express a preference for its employment. Dynamism as the name for a mental mechanism is not uncommonly used, and indeed might replace the older term were it not so well established.

(2) Normal versus pathologic consequences

It is important to bear in mind that the mental mechanisms or dynamisms are widely present in both normal, healthy human psychologic function as well as in that which is unhealthy and pathologic. As indicated earlier, we find them operating in varying degrees in every human being; their use is by no means confined to those individuals who might ordinarily be regarded as mentally ill.

Thus, when they are found to be present and identifiable, this by no means constitutes *a priori* evidence that a psychopathological condition is present. Their presence is to be regarded as pathologic or normal in varying degrees according to:

(1) The manner in which they are employed.
(2) How psychologically efficacious they prove to be.
(3) Whether the net contribution they make to the total individual psychologic economy is constructive or destructive.

(3) Foundation blocks of modern psychiatry

Our present study will be devoted to the mental mechanisms and particularly to several representative ones for many of the foregoing reasons. The mechanisms are basic in current theories of dynamic psychiatry. Knowledge of these intrapsychic processes is essential in order that one's knowledge of psychiatry may rest on a solid foundation.

An adequate conception of human motivation and psychopathology requires a working understanding of these vital defensively-intended endeavors. Such an understanding is a *must* for competent psychotherapy. The dynamisms or mental mechanisms are foundation blocks of modern dynamic psychiatry.

3. THE MENTAL MECHANISMS

A. DEFINITION

In the light of our discussion thus far, a formal definition is now possible. A mental mechanism or dynamism is *a specific defensive process, operating outside of and beyond conscious awareness. It is automatically and unconsciously employed in the endeavor to secure resolution of emotional conflict, relief from emotional tension, and to avert or allay anxiety. A given dynamism is evoked by the ego as an attempted means of coping with an otherwise consciously-intolerable situation.*

This definition will apply throughout our study. It should be automatically considered a part of each individual definition for any given dynamism.

Man is able to avoid or avert painful emotions or awareness of them by the employment of mental mechanisms, *unconsciously.* As referred to earlier, there is in addition such a thing as the *conscious* and deliberate use of essentially similar endeavors. These are often named identically. However, for the process to be truly a mental mechanism and in accord with our above definition, it must operate outside of the conscious awareness of the person concerned, that is, be an unconscious endeavor.

TABLE 1

THE MENTAL MECHANISMS

The mental mechanisms are unconsciously developed patterns of psychologic defense. They are also known as *dynamisms* or *ego defenses.* They may be divided into major and minor groups according to:

10

Table 1 (continued)

(1) Relative clarity of delineation and identification.
(2) Ease of recognition.
(3) General professional acceptance.
(4) Level of concurrence as to existence and function.

I. The Major Dynamisms

There are 22 major mental mechanisms, as follows. These are also known as *prime* or *primary dynamisms*.

1. Compensation *
2. Conversion
3. Denial
4. Displacement
5. Dissociation
6. Fantasy
7. Idealization
8. Identification *
9. Incorporation
10. Internalization
11. Introjection
12. Inversion *
13. Projection
14. Rationalization
15. Reaction Formation
16. Regression
17. Repression *
18. Restitution *
19. Sublimation *
20. Substitution
21. Symbolization
22. Undoing

II. The Minor Dynamisms

The following are the internal defensive operations which, at various times, have been mentioned as mental mechanisms. In view of the less distinct delineation possible, and an absence of general professional agreement, I would suggest we refer to them as the *minor* or *secondary* mental mechanisms.

1. Absolution
2. Atonement and Penance
3. Compromise Formation
4. Condensation
5. Convergence
6. Deferment
7. Devaluation
8. Distortion
9. Extension
10. Externalization
11. Fainting
12. Fire Drill
13. Generalization
14. Intellectualization
15. Isolation
16. Overdetermination
17. Personal Invulnerability
18. Replacement
19. Retribution
20. Retrospective (or Retroactive) Devaluation
21. Reversal
22. Splitting
23. Withdrawal

III. Special Reactions and Combinations of Dynamisms

A number of complex reactions and combination of ego defenses can be observed with sufficient frequency to warrant their recognition, description, and study. This has occurred as noted by the following examples and will doubtless take place increasingly.

1. The King David Reaction
   (a) Positive
   (b) Negative
2. Righteous Indignation
3. Character Defenses

---

* Representative dynamisms included in the present study.

B. THE MENTAL MECHANISMS, MAJOR AND MINOR

The mental mechanisms are detailed in *Table 1*. The first group of 22 dynamisms can be more or less clearly delineated. These are the internal defense processes, the identification of which has the greatest general acceptance professionally. I would like to propose our referring to them as *major, prime,* or *primary* mental mechanisms.

A number of other processes can be less distinctly delineated and identified. For this reason we can regard them as *minor* or *secondary* mental mechanisms. With these there is considerably less professional acceptance and concurrence. They accordingly receive less attention and emphasis.

A review of the psychiatric literature indicates some differences of opinion about some of the mental mechanisms. Some authorities have used different names for the same process, failed to recognize some of them, or have assigned to them overlapping meanings and functions. The overall trend, however, has been gradually toward more general agreement as to function and meaning, and more precision as to their definition and usage. It is hoped that the present study may make some contribution to this useful trend, in the interest of more accurate communication and scientific progress in this field.

To a considerable extent these differences as indicated are more apparent than basic and real. Some of them have been present simply through such things as personal choice, the evolution of individual terminology in a rapidly developing field, or because of practice and usage in a particular training center. The primary defensive operations remain the same regardless of our individual professional variations in viewpoint. Indeed, the latter serve useful purposes in a scientific discipline by fostering continuing inquiry and by constantly raising questions for further consideration. Stagnation is prevented and avenues are thereby offered for constructive evolution, and for possible advances through new modifications of terminology, thought, and view.

C. OPERATION IS USUALLY IN COMBINATION AND OVERLAPPING

In any thorough discussion of the mental mechanisms, they must be taken up and considered separately. This must be done in the interests of clarity, convenience, and simplicity. However, we should keep in mind that in actuality they are rarely found functioning completely separately and independently. As a consequence we

12

cannot really isolate mental mechanisms save for demonstration and study. Generally they act in concert, and are seldom encountered clinically as isolated phenomena. There is also a good deal of overlapping in our concepts concerning them.

There are many examples of overlapping. For instance, the interesting mechanism of Idealization is often most intimately associated in its operation with the mechanism of Identification. Substitution usually operates in concert with Displacement. A number of mechanisms may be observed to function in the general service of Denial.

Inversion and Reaction Formation operate in similar fashion, are difficult to differentiate, and often enough require the drawing of a fine line of distinction in their separate delineation. Incorporation, Introjection, and Internalization are analogous, subserve similar psychologic functions, have overlapping usage, and may be nearly impossible to distinguish. In *Case 1,* Rationalization is seen to operate in the service of Denial. Projection in *Case 2* likewise promotes Denial, and may be viewed as assisting in a type of Rationalization as well. The mechanisms in both of these examples aid and support the maintenance of Repression.

The observer will accordingly find that two or more of these complex internal processes will often function concurrently in order to produce a common defensively-intended effect. Basically what they are attempting to do is (*a*) to allay or prevent anxiety, (*b*) resolve emotional conflict, (*c*) combat emotional discomfort and pain, and/or (*d*) prevent *de*repression (the return into consciousness of ideas, thoughts, emotions, desires, fantasies, or wishes that have been earlier banished from conscious awareness because they proved too painful, and unacceptable; that is, intolerable).

D. VITAL ROLE IN HEALTH AND ILLNESS

(1) Contributions to adjustment, well-being, and social progress

The vital role which mental mechanisms play in emotional well-being becomes increasingly clear to us. Mental mechanisms can contribute constructively to emotional equanimity. One's satisfactions in living may be increased as a consequence to their operation. One's personal and professional effectiveness and efficiency may be enhanced.

It is often through their exaggeration or overdevelopment that trouble occurs. When the operation is in proper balance, contributions are made to emotional health and to individual growth and maturity. Inevitably the unconscious adoption and development of mental mechanisms and patterns of reaction enters into character formation. The various constellations of character traits which are to be seen, are influenced by, and also in turn likely influence, the dynamisms employed. Further, these intrapsychic defense processes can also provide a useful kind of emotional "safety valve." Through them, otherwise intolerable internal pressures can be absorbed, neutralized, or provided a consciously acceptable outward expression. This can be of considerable benefit.

Finally, and also through their operation, social benefits can accrue. For example, one may observe how energy from instinctual drives can become changed and redirected through the mechanism of Sublimation into channels which are of considerable social usefulness. Further examples of these possible constructive consequences are numerous.

(2) Self-defeating consequences

We are even more interested in this study in the possible self-defeating and destructive consequences. In accord with the principles of the important *Attention Hypothesis,** our interest tends to be rather selectively drawn toward those resulting areas of concern, difficulty, and trouble. These are developments which can lead to, or contribute to pathology. Thus, through the exaggeration and overdevelopment of various ones of the dynamisms, or as a further step in the progression of new internal psychologic defenses in the event of the inadequacy or failure of existing ones, symptom formation can result. In this manner the psychogenesis of all kinds of emotional illness may be facilitated. In analogous fashion character defensive traits may slowly develop which are less healthful, or existing ones may become exaggerated in an unhealthy and self-defeating manner.

Thus the net result of employing a dynamism may well be self-defeat. This has been noted (and illustrated in *Case 2*) and will be

---

* The *Attention Hypothesis* points out that one's attention tends to be selectively, automatically, and irresistibly drawn toward one's personal areas of greatest interest and concern.

Things which trouble us or cause painful feelings will likely be more a matter for attention than are more neutral areas. There is a magnetic kind of attraction for our attention which is present for us in matters of concern and trouble. Such areas are even likely often enough to take priority over pleasurable ones.

further discussed. Hereby the dynamism may even help to ensure the very thing which contributed to the initiating intolerable distress in the first place! A vicious circle can ensue. Distress, or the threat of distress brings into play the mechanism, which increases distress, which in turn reinforces the defensive processes against it, and so on. Ultimately, in some cases, the use of one or more dynamisms may become so all-pervasive in a person's life and adjustment as to lead to this becoming almost literally a "way of life," in, and of itself. Such a way of life may constitute a severe neurosis, one which may be terribly limiting and pathologic. Another possible inimical sequella is the facilitation of a serious and pathologic kind of regressive trend.

Finally, insight and a more accurate self-picture are clouded and obscured for the sick patient, as well as for the person who is relatively healthy emotionally. The defense is developed unconsciously and so maintained. Should its operation dawn upon conscious awareness, its effectiveness is likely lost. Hence the patient will indeed guard it well. This helps explain the resistances encountered in therapy. This also brings us to brief mention of another important concept of psychiatry.

4. THE SECONDARY DEFENSE

(1) The symptom (Dynamism or character trait), a defense in itself, is in turn, i.e. secondarily, defended

A mental mechanism is often, perhaps most often, the first unconscious endeavor called into play to meet psychologic danger. It is a *primary* defense. Most emotional symptoms may be also regarded as primary defenses. Many of the character defenses (character or personality traits) may be so considered. Now, as indicated above, once a defense is called into play and has become operative, it becomes a vital matter to the person concerned. He unconsciously seeks to maintain it, sometimes at almost all costs. Part of this requires that its unconscious nature be maintained. Often enough it will not fully stand up under objective scrutiny, hence its effectiveness will likely be impaired if it comes into consciousness. It is therefore hardly surprising that *the primary defense becomes in turn defended.*

This is the important and useful concept of the Secondary Defense. All subsequent endeavors—conscious and unconscious—

15

which seek to maintain and preserve the operation of any mental mechanism, symptom, or character defense fit into this broad category of secondary defense. In other words, the dynamism or symptom, a defense itself, is in turn defended (*See also* later reference, pages 178, 190–91, and 241).

(2) Therapy and resistance: preservation of symptoms by secondary defenses

The nature and means of such a secondary defense vary widely. For example, a patient may insist that a physical basis simply must be at the root of his conversion pain or paralysis, refusing to even consider the possibility of any emotional contribution, exaggeration, or basis. Obviously this may for most practical purposes block therapeutic study, preserving his tragically self-defeating, but desperately clung to, symptom-defenses. Often the more handicapping the symptom, the more grim and vigorous its defense.

Secondary defenses may operate in many far more subtle ways. Much of the resistance which one inevitably encounters in psychotherapy is a secondary defensive endeavor, seeking to guard the *status quo* of existing psychologic defenses, regardless of their self-defeating consequences. There are myriad ways in which secondary defenses operate.

5. INTENDED FUNCTIONS OF THE DYNAMISMS

(1) Potential, intent, and goal

We have seen how the potential for serious emotional illness is present in the operation of certain dynamisms. This is certainly far from the intent. It is also interesting to note that their unconscious operation constitutes both an advantage from one point of view, and a disadvantage from another. It is an advantage, indeed a necessity since, if maintained as an unconscious operation, it is not then subject to rationality. Its existence is not then threatened by the possibility of objective evaluation and judgment. On the other hand the unconscious status of the process places the person most vitally concerned in a helpless position. He is at a decided disadvantage. An inability to make possible constructive modifications is an inevitable accompaniment of his inability to recognize. He is indeed impotent.

16

What is unconsciously sought is an adjustment to life. Each individual seeks to satisfactorily adapt himself to his environment. Most important aspects of environment of course are those which are interpersonal. One wishes to avoid psychic discomfort and pain; to secure a measure of psychologic homeostasis. In general one desires to secure emotional stability and equanimity.

We have already referred to the goal of conflict resolution. There are several major ways in which the mental mechanisms may undertake this. For instance, through a dynamism an alternate, more consciously-acceptable solution may be attempted. By such mechanisms as Displacement and Substitution, something emotionally and psychically tolerable may be substituted for something which the person concerned finds consciously intolerable. Anxiety is an exceedingly unpleasant experience. Its control, prevention, or avoidance is an ever present goal. Its abolition aids in the broader goal of increased personal security.

Mental mechanisms attempt to provide acceptable compromises. These are needed whenever personal drives, goals, needs, or wishes are present which are impossible and/or intolerable to satisfy because of opposing personal or social standards. The maintenance and reenforcement of Repression can also be an important function of mental mechanisms. In this type of service, the process can fit into our earlier concept of secondary defense.

(2) The bolstering of intrapsychic defenses and the maintenance of ego integrity

Finally, we view the dynamism and its intended goals in the light of its being essentially an ego function, and its vital service to be the maintaining of ego integrity. The bolstering of internal psychologic defenses helps to combat disruptive effects and aids ego integration. Intolerable instinctual drives have a disintegrating and dissociative effect. Their impact is blunted and their energy absorbed through the operation of various dynamisms. Herein the development of the mental mechanism is a major emotional and psychologic response to this internal danger; the danger that the consciously intolerable wish or drive might not be kept in control. As noted earlier, this may be regarded as analogous to the physical and physiologic preparations for "fight" or "flight" which may occur in response to a danger or a threat essentially external in origin.

The following is a brief tabulation of the principal defensively-intended goals of the mental mechanisms, and some of the beneficial and the injurious consequences of their employment.

17

TABLE 2

FUNCTIONS AND CONSEQUENCES OF THE MENTAL MECHANISMS

The mental mechanisms or dynamisms are protectively-intended endeavors of the ego. They are specific intrapsychic defensive processes which operate outside of and beyond conscious awareness. They are developed in the service of ego integration and preservation. This table summarizes their principal intended functions, and certain possible vital consequences of their use.

I. Intended Functions of the Dynamisms

The functions which a given dynamism attempts to subserve may be single, multiple, or overlapping. Likewise, several mental mechanisms may operate in a symbiotic kind of relationship, to each other's mutual advantage and reenforcement; toward the same goal. The degree of effectiveness and the success achieved in these intrapsychic endeavors is, of course, highly variable. One or several goals might be sought. We might describe these rather generally, as follows:

(1) A satisfactory adjustment to life; the attainment or the improvement of one's adaptation to his environment—especially including the interpersonal.

(2) Avoidance of psychic discomfort and pain.

(3) The securing, maintenance, or both of emotional stability and equanimity (psychologic homeostasis).

(4) The enhancement or preservation of self-esteem.

(5) The resolution of emotional (psychic) conflict, such as by:
  (a) Attempting to provide alternative, consciously acceptable solutions, or
  (b) Substituting something emotionally tolerable for that which is otherwise consciously intolerable.

(6) The lessening of the subjective experiencing of anxiety; allaying or preventing anxious feelings.

(7) The increase of personal security.

(8) The securing of acceptable compromises where personal drives, goals, needs, or wishes are present which are impossible, intolerable, or both because of directly opposing personal or social standards.

(9) The maintenance of ego integrity; ego defense and integration, especially through:
  (a) Bolstering psychologic defenses, and
  (b) Meeting the destructive, disintegrating impact of *internal* danger. Herein is included the development of mental mechanisms as major emotional and psychologic response.

18

Table 2 (continued)

This is analogous to the physical and physiologic preparation for "fight" or "flight," which occur in response to *external* danger or threat.

II. Possible Consequences of the Employment of the Dynamisms

   A. Constructive contributions to:

      (1) Emotional equanimity; to effectiveness and satisfactions in living.

      (2) Determination of character structure; the development of the individual constellations of character defensive (personality) traits.

      (3) Emotional health and maturity.

      (4) Providing an emotional "safety valve"; facilitation of an outwardly disguised, substitutive, and consciously-acceptable expression of otherwise intolerable pressures.

      (5) Social benefit; redirection of the energy of instinctual drives, as through Sublimation, into socially more acceptable and useful channels.

   B. Self-defeating and destructive consequences

      (1) Symptom formation, contributing to all kinds of emotional illnesses, especially through:

         (a) Their exaggeration and overdevelopment, and

         (b) As a further step in defensive progression, in the event of their failure or inadequacy to cope with the threat.

      (2) Unhealthy exaggeration of character defensive traits.

      (3) Self-defeat; may help to ensure (as in *Case 2*) the very thing which contributed to the initiating intolerable distress in the first place. A vicious circle may be set up.

      (4) The hampering of insight: inability to see oneself clearly, whether one is emotionally sick or relatively healthy.

      (5) May lead to regression.

      (6) May develop into what is almost literally "a way of life"; a severe neurosis which may be terribly limiting and pathologic.

---

6. "LOWER ORDER" AND "HIGHER ORDER" DEFENSES

In the study of psychologic defenses I have found a concept which I have developed, concerning the "level" of their operation to be a matter of considerable interest and some importance. Thus, certain defenses operate on a more primitive level than others. These are the *lower order* or *more primitive* defenses. Others are less primitive and more advanced. These are the *higher order* or *more advanced* defenses. A number of the mental mechanisms fit rather clearly into one group or the other. The neuroses may also be so classified.

A. THE MORE PRIMITIVE DYNAMISMS

(1) Primitive Dynamisms described: massive, deeply unconscious, lower order, less developed, magical quality, primordial

The more primitive or lower order dynamisms are more massive in their operation. The emotional level of these processes tends to be very deeply unconscious. They operate more automatically, and conscious efforts in a similar direction are more widely separate from the unconscious dynamism. Their use is more likely to be observed in less mature individuals. They tend to be more prominent as primordial mechanisms; in infancy and in the very young.

The mental mechanisms of Incorporation and Repression, particularly the *primary* Repressions, are excellent examples of the lower order or primitive dynamism. They are quite automatic and are deeply unconscious. Conscious efforts at Incorporation are rare, as well as different from the unconscious process. Repression of consciously unacceptable material is so completely different from the conscious efforts at forgetting that we use a different term altogether: *suppression.* Suppression is the conscious attempt to subjugate unacceptable thoughts or desires, in which one is clearly aware of the attempt. In contradistinction, Repression is automatic and unconscious. Incorporation and Repression are especially prominent as primordial mechanisms, and are most operative and important in the very early years.

(2) Greater frequency in early years and in the less mature

Other mental mechanisms also more readily fit into the category of lower order, more primitive, or lower level defenses. These include Conversion, Denial, Displacement, Dissociation, Symbolization, and Undoing. This group of dynamisms has a more magical quality.

20

The more immature, impulsive, and emotionally labile person is more apt to employ ones belonging to this group, although this is not an absolute and certain finding. They are also encountered more often in the very early years.

B. THE MORE ADVANCED MECHANISMS

(1) Highly developed, complex and less primitive nature

The more advanced and developed, or higher order mental mechanisms tend to operate in a more complex and involved fashion. Their emotional level of operation tends at times to be less deeply unconscious. They are less massive and are somewhat less automatic, seeming at times to develop more gradually. Conscious efforts in a similar direction are closely analogous and the name for the unconscious process and the conscious effort in the same direction are usually identical. They operate at all ages and are commonly seen in the older and more mature individual.

The mental mechanisms of Rationalization and Projection are good examples of the higher order, or advanced dynamisms. The higher order processes are relatively more superficial and tend to operate on a more superficial level of unconsciousness. Conscious efforts in these directions are common, and are so identical in their aim as to lead the one to practically merge into the other. As with the dynamism of Rationalization, both conscious effort and unconscious dynamism bear identical names. Each may be seen to operate at any age. They are less massive, less automatic, less primitive, and less magical in their operation than the lower order types of dynamisms. Both tend to be more complex and developed.

(2) Greater frequency in later years, and in the more mature

They operate in conjunction with several types of emotional illness, with a tendency in turn to contribute to the psychopathology of the more advanced or higher order forms of neurotic reaction. There is also the chance that the higher order types of mechanisms will more likely be found to be employed by the more mature, less impulsive, and at least outwardly more emotionally stable kind of person, although this is also not an absolute finding.

Other mental mechanisms which fit into the category of higher order, or more advanced defenses, include Compensation, Intellectualization, Restitution, and Sublimation.

C. THE NEUROSES

As noted, this concept also finds applicability as to the various types of neurotic reaction.

(1) Lower order

Those which fit best into the lower order category, or more primitive group include (a) Conversion Reactions, with the Somatic Conversions (Conversion Hysteria) most typical, (b) Dissociative Reaction, (c) Phobic Reactions, (d) Soterial Reactions, (e) some of the Neuroses following Trauma, and possibly in some cases of (f) Hypochondriasis (Hygeiaphrontis).

(2) Higher order

The neurotic reactions which fit best into the higher order, or more advanced type include: (a) Character Neuroses, (b) most of the Anxiety Reactions, (c) Depressions, (d) Fatigue Reactions, (e) most cases of Hypochondriasis, (f) some cases of Neuroses following Trauma, and (g) the Obsessive-Compulsive Reactions.

7. INTELLIGENCE AND EMOTIONAL PROBLEMS

A. EVOLVING CONCEPTIONS

Not too many decades ago, it was fashionable to believe that emotional illness was far more likely to occur where intelligence was limited; or was perhaps almost restricted to such persons. With this kind of belief of course, prejudice flourished. Currently, few still subscribe to this myth. The relative level of emotional difficulties has little correlation with the level of intelligence. What correlation we can determine is of a different nature than that implied above.

The person who is emotionally ill is not stupid. He is sick. He has not become sick through lack of intelligence or stupidity, nor does he remain so for any such reason. Nor is he ill through a lack of will power. His illness has come about as a consequence of the ineffective operation of unconscious defenses which he originally developed automatically in response to unconscious danger or threat. He may become ill because the defenses which he has elaborated are overwhelmed by a sudden overpowering internal threat, or because the defenses themselves have been unwittingly exaggerated to the point of handicap, self-defeat, or even gross pathology. Defenses are automatically erected, and the patient has little or no voluntary or conscious control over them.

Actually, with certain types of emotional illness (for example, Emotional Depression), we see an increased incidence among the better educated, more intellectually favored people. The development of certain kinds of emotional conflicts, and the utilization of particular types of intrapsychic defense mechanisms seem to be more suitable for those endowed with superior intelligence and greater intellectual capacity.

The only other correlation which we might suggest is that between the type of defense utilized and the general level of education; intellectual capacity; and sophistication. Herein we may note a more frequent tendency toward the utilization of the more primitive or lower order defenses by those less favored. However, even this is subject to fairly frequent exceptions.

B. SUPERIOR INTELLIGENCE IS NO PROTECTION

It becomes clear that superior intelligence is by no means a protection against emotional illness. I have worked with many patients in psychotherapy whose intellectual endowments were considerably above average, including a few whose I.Q.s indicated the genius level. Through my experience as a therapist, this point has been amply and repeatedly brought home to me. The experience of others in the field is parallel.

The origin of the illness thus lies in the sphere of the emotions, and not in the sphere of the intellect. The term "emotional illness" is of importance therefore both in indicating the origin of the problems and in correctly directing attention away from anything concerned with the intellect. I would accordingly find the term "emotional illness" preferable to "mental illness," which can more readily convey a mistaken connotation as to the origin of the difficulty.

Everyone has emotions, and some share of painful feelings. It is part of being human. Everyone has problems. These may vary in extent, kind, and degree, from time to time, and from person to person, but no one remains constantly calm and untroubled. The differences between people in these areas often is more one of quantity than one of quality.

Psychologic defenses which are evoked in response to one's problems are individual, and some correlations are possible, as noted above. It is also true that certain defenses and types of illness interfere with the best application of one's intellectual faculties, and can substantially restrict the exercise of one's best judgment. The overall process of maturation may also be impeded. However, one should note that many brilliant and socially valuable citizens are often highly neurotic people. Their neurotic drives may have contributed to or even led to their successes.

C. NO PLACE FOR PREJUDICE

(1) Need for respect and understanding

In line with the foregoing comments and because of many cogent reasons, the reader should have an adequate and kindly respect for the emotionally sick patient. Such respect is best enhanced through more understanding of the ways in which such illness develops. Emotional illness is a process from which the unaided patient is powerless to extricate himself. His character defenses or neurotic symptoms constitute a steel trap. The sound approach is through securing more knowledge about the purposes, nature, and operation of human psychologic defenses. Such knowledge leaves no room for prejudice. Our survey of the mental mechanisms is intended to help in this regard.

(2) Normality and illness are relative

Several findings stand out as more or less counter to some of the continuing bias which lingers on stubbornly in a few scattered quarters toward, and about emotional illness. First, in the field of emotional or mental health the so-called normal is a relative matter. Further, it is somewhat difficult to define, and it gradually merges into the borderline, which in turn gradually merges on into illness.

The use of the mental mechanisms may contribute to health. On the other hand they may gradually and almost imperceptibly merge into the pathologic manifestations of a neurosis, character neurosis, or functional psychosis.

(3) Similarity of psychic defenses

Second, from the standpoint of their psychologic defenses, people are not really very different. They use the same psychologic defenses; the identical mental mechanisms. The only differences here are in amount, extent, and/or in the individual combination of their employment. These differences are far more ones of degree rather than of kind. This of course does not deny that such differ-

24

ences can be most important as to effects and results. Finally, emotional problems are indeed universal, as earlier noted.

In modern science, in medicine, and among a sophisticated laity, there is truly no longer any place for uninformed prejudice about mental health. As we currently view the patient who suffers with cancer; it is more a matter of "There, but for the grace of God, go I."

8. EMOTIONAL OR MENTAL HEALTH: A DEFINITION

It would seem incomplete to conclude this introduction to the many interesting mental mechanisms without undertaking a definition of emotional health. Accordingly we may define emotional health as *a state of being which is relative, rather than absolute.* In general, *the person who is emotionally healthy has effected a reasonably satisfactory integration of his instinctual drives.* He has worked out psychologically harmonious solutions for them which are acceptable to himself, and to his social milieu.

This is reflected in the following ways:

(1) In the satisfactory nature of his interpersonal relationships.
(2) In his cheerful and willing acceptance of social responsibilities.
(3) In his level of satisfaction in living.
(4) In his flexibility in adjusting to new situations.
(5) In his effectiveness—his actual achievements, in relation to his realistic capacities and endowment.
(6) In the absence of handicapping and limiting symptoms, or character defense traits.
(7) In his achievement of a reasonable degree of emotional equanimity.
(8) In his ability to react constructively to threat or danger.
(9) In the relative level of maturity which he has achieved.
(10) In his integration and intellectual functioning.

Among important assets which might be listed, one hopes that the emotionally healthy individual possesses some reasonable measure of the following:

(1) Cheerfulness.
(2) Ability to enjoy work.
(3) Efficiency.

(4) "Tempered Emotions"—extreme emotions in any direction are neither experienced nor displayed.
(5) Tolerance for differing views.
(6) Ability to change opinions.
(7) Capacity for love and understanding.
(8) Enjoyment of play—leisure and spare time activities.
(9) Achievement of realistic goals.
(10) Ability to say "Yes" or "No", as appropriate.
(11) Reasonable satisfaction in living—and with life.
(12) Ability to accept criticism or blame.

In an assessment of emotional health one may further evaluate such factors as:

(1) The appropriateness of emotional response to realistically evaluated situations.
(2) An ability to experience and to express appropriate emotions.
(3) A good level of self-understanding, together with reasonable ability to recognize one's emotional reactions, motivations, and their bases.
(4) A history of successful interpersonal relations: family, friends; professional, business, and social relationships.
(5) A level of health interest which is constructive.
(6) Acceptance of responsibility.
(7) The ability to properly safeguard one's own best interests.
(8) Application of the Golden Rule.

CHAPTER 2

REPRESSION

. . . assignment to the unconscious . . .

1. THE NATURE OF REPRESSION

A. AN AUTOMATIC AND CONSCIOUSLY EFFORTLESS PROCESS

(1) Repression's major role in emotional illness and health

Repression or its threatened failure is the precursor of all the mental mechanisms, and has a fathering role in all the neuroses, character neuroses, and functional psychoses. It is accordingly appropriate that we consider it first in our present survey of several representative dynamisms. Through its ego sustaining and protective effects, repression plays a vital role in maintaining emotional health. The mental mechanisms are the foundation—the building blocks—of modern dynamic psychiatry and are basic to an understanding of human behavior.[28, 29] In a continuing analogy, repression is the cornerstone of psychiatry.

Repression is an automatic and consciously effortless kind of memory loss or forgetting. As such, it seems a simple enough kind of process. Through it, ideas, impulses, and emotional feelings which are consciously repugnant and thereby intolerable to the individual for various reasons, are assigned to a deeper layer of the psyche, which we call the unconscious. Thereby, the unconscious becomes the repository for much that has been painful in fantasy, ideation, or experience; for that which has proven to be consciously intolerable.

(2) A key concept in the behavioral sciences

What is repressed, however, does not remain dormant nor necessarily quiescent. Although thus submerged and ordinarily inaccessible to voluntary conscious recall, the repressed material remains active, emotionally charged, and potent. As such, it can contribute to trouble if (*a*) new emotional dangers or threats place

28

too great a burden on the repressing process, (*b*) internal pressures become too great for the continued containment of repressed material, or (*c*) the repressing forces become too weak.

An understanding of the concept of Repression is very important in the study of personality development and maturation, character trait formation, emotional illness and emotional health, human behavior, and living. Repression is the keystone in the arch of our modern conceptions of psychology, dynamic psychiatry, and the behavioral sciences.

B. DEFINITION

(1) The relegation of the intolerable to the unconscious

We can define Repression as *the automatic, effortless, and involuntary relegation of consciously repugnant or intolerable ideas, impulses, and feelings into the unconscious.*[28, 29] Following this defensively and protectively intended process, such material is not ordinarily subject to voluntary conscious recall. Repressed material includes data which never really entered consciousness, in addition to that which, having once been in conscious awareness, has subsequently been assigned or relegated to the unconscious through its Repression.

Considered as a mental mechanism or dynamism, Repression is the most widely used. Actually, it is a universally employed process of psychologic defense. Repression involves forgetting and memory loss, but more than this, the memory loss is a "directed" and purposeful kind. It is *unconsciously* directed, however, by psychic expediency, and its purpose is ego defense. Conflictual, disturbing, and painful wishes, thoughts, and urges are thereby banished from consciousness.

Repression acts in the service of conflict resolution, seeking surcease for an embattled and harassed ego. The motive force for Repression ultimately comes from anxiety, or the threat of anxiety.[29] Similarly, these same needs help to ensure continued Repression. Subjective anxiety is usually the signal when derepression threatens. At this juncture, other mechanisms also may be called into operation. Should these prove inadequate as defenses, the onset of emotional symptoms may occur, an emotional illness may even be initiated, or an existing one aggravated.

29

(2) Repression a basic process, particularly active in earlier years

This very important process is particularly active throughout the very early years. However, it also continues to operate throughout life. Repression is a primitive and first-line type of ego defense which acts in the service of lessening, resolving, and preventing emotional conflict, and consequent anxiety. Repression is a basic process, since it necessarily precedes the operation of nearly every other mental mechanism. Many of the other mental mechanisms are called into operation as reenforcements of Repression. If its classification is attempted, it clearly belongs best with what I have proposed to call the less advanced or lower order group of mechanisms.

From our introductory discussion thus far, one can see how very important the concept of Repression has become in medicine, psychiatry, and the behavioral sciences. Repression is today one of the cardinal tenets of modern dynamic psychiatry. By Repression unacceptable thoughts are expelled from consciousness. It is the fundamental defense mechanism of the ego. In addition to its vital and basic role in emotional illness and health, an understanding of Repression is very important to understanding the many factors in memory and recall.

(3) Repression an automatic, effortless, and active process

According to Slotkin,[45] Repression is an unconscious kind of inhibition. Brown [9] regards Repression as the mechanism of forcing the unpleasant part of a conflict into the unconscious. Menninger [37] notes also that Repression is the "holding back of ideas and wishes from consciousness." This does not mean holding something back from someone else, but holding it back from oneself.

To Anna Freud [18] Repression "consists in the withholding or the expulsion of an idea or affect from the conscious ego." We may well regard this as the essence of Repression. Most authorities will agree that Repression is the automatic forgetting of ideas, complexes, or needs which, consciously, are distasteful or intolerable. Repression is a basic and primitive psychic defense. Other dynamisms are frequently related to it, often in a supplemental role.

I have defined Repression as automatic and effortless—and so it is, from the *subjective and conscious* standpoints. Accordingly,

I do not consider it at all inconsistent to regard it also as an active force. It must be, to so successfully oppose the energy surge and impetus of intolerable and prohibited instinctual (id) drives. Repression is an ego function acting unconsciously in response to prohibitions by the self and/or through social mores and standards.

C. MEMORY AND REPRESSION

There is a very close relationship between memory and Repression. Coleman [10] regards Repression as the mechanism by which "dangerous and intolerable memories are kept out of consciousness." English and Finch [11] define Repression as the "forgetting of either internal urgings or external events which would be painful if they reached consciousness." O'Kelly and Muckler [41] describe Repression as "selective forgetting, or loss of awareness of thoughts, memories, wishes, that would give pain or discomfort." Hunt [23] sees it as a way of "pushing disturbing memory out of consciousness."

White [49] looks upon Repression as "the forgetting or ejecting from consciousness of memories of threat and especially the ejection from awareness of impulses in the self that might have objectionable consequences."

We shall observe repeatedly the close relationships of memory and Repression.

D. EARLY PROMINENCE AND UNIVERSAL ACTIVITY

I have noted that Repression is a very important process that is particularly active throughout the early years, as well as universal. Klein [26] points out that the normal as well as the abnormal child makes use of Repression to deal with his conflicts. Schmideberg has stressed the point that this defense mechanism is already at work in the first months of life. While it is particularly active in the very early years, we must bear in mind that it also continues throughout the life of the individual, as already noted.

Landis and Bolles [27] agree that Repression is one of the most common defense mechanisms. They note also the idea of a degree or level of effectiveness by describing it as the "more or less successful exclusion of painful and unpleasant material from expression in behavior or mental life."

E. ENERGY-LADEN AND POTENT

(1) Repressed material continues to seek expression

A most significant aspect of Repression has been mentioned in that although various wishes, needs, thoughts, urges, or memories may have been relegated to the unconscious by Repression, and the individual is no longer aware of them, their dynamic possibilities do not stop there. They are not non-existent; they are but slumbering. In this analogy this is a troubled, restless, and uneasy kind of sleep!

Thus, while intolerable desires or urges may have been relegated to the unconscious, they are by no means inactive there. They are energy-laden. They remain potent. Sadler [43] characterized Repression as "the unconscious rejection of perceptions and ideas because of their painful and disagreeable content." The repressed material "is submerged into the unconscious, but remains dynamic" . . . Repression "does not destroy the power of an instinct or impulse" . . . and "such frustrated energy still seeks expression."

Orgel [42] sees in Repression a "defense against unwelcome thoughts and desires," through which they are "banished from awareness," and although they continue dormant, they "may generate emotional tension." . . . "Repression is the process of keeping down emotionally tinged memories which are in conflict, and which would cause added conflict if they were permitted to enter consciousness."

(2) Energy required to maintain Repression

Although Repression may prevent conscious conflict, it can also bring about unconscious conflict. It is part of our concept of Repression that "each unacceptable drive or impulse that undergoes repression requires a certain amount of energy to maintain it in its repressed state." [30]

For Menninger,[38] Repression is "a device used by the mind to deal with the conflicts that arise between the instincts; and between the individual and his environment." Through its use, "that part of the conflict which the rest of the personality does not approve is repressed. Yet there is a continual striving on the part of the repressed tendencies to escape."

These repressed strivings may attempt to escape by various means, especially by undergoing modifications through the operation of other mental mechanisms. They may also, of course, secure expression in disguised, modified, and symbolic forms.

F. REPRESSION AND SUPPRESSION

(1) The conscious, deliberate, and effortful nature of Suppression

The terms Repression and Suppression are frequently confused in lay usage. In the interests of clarity, it may be worthwhile to point out the distinction. Suppression is the process in which one has made *conscious* efforts to forget, control, and restrain; one thus seeks to subjugate unacceptable thoughts or desires, with the individual concerned being clearly aware of the attempt. By Suppression, one directs his attention away from undesirable thoughts, objects, or feelings. It is a consciously directed effort to banish from awareness; a conscious effort to forget. By suppression one seeks to subdue and to quell. In the use of this term then, there is an implied conscious effort to keep down and to restrain; to try to forget.

Repression, on the other hand, is the *automatic* relegation from consciousness of the unacceptable thought or wish. It is an unconscious and involuntary process. There may be no conscious effort; no awareness of the wish or striving, nor of its unacceptability. When something has actually been successfully banished from consciousness, it has been repressed; we usually employ suppression as the term to describe the conscious effort in this direction.

(2) Unconscious accomplishment of Repression

Menninger [39] writes, when "we speak of suppression . . . we refer to the deliberate, conscious renunciation of certain wishes or temptations. Repression is a very different matter. It is unconsciously accomplished, and what one has repressed he is unconscious of; he does not even know that he has repressed anything at all."

In other words, suppression is conscious, deliberate and effortful. To Freud, "successful" suppression meant an idea would "vanish completely," that is, successful suppression would equate Repression.

2. HISTORICAL NOTES

A. A CONCEPT OF HISTORICAL VALIDATION

(1) Concepts and their antecedents

I have found the study of the origins of psychologic concepts and terms a fascinating occupation. Nearly always it seems, if one searches enough through the literature, an antecedent can be found for almost any given psychologic concept or term; one which was not previously suspected. This has occurred sufficiently often during my work on definitions and terminology to wonder where the line really should be drawn as to the point of conception or introduction.

Usually, drawing such a line is likely to pose some difficulty, if all the facts be known. There is still more of a problem if one considers including some of the direct and indirect influences of the supposed initiator's teachers, his contacts with his colleagues, and seeds of ideas which may have been inadvertently planted through his reading and study. These can be subtle; and can also operate unconsciously. Conceptions frequently appear more to develop, to evolve, and to grow, often through successive generations.

In my own work with psychiatric theory, these kinds of considerations have led me to the postulation of a *Concept of Historical Validation.*

(2) The contribution of prior evidence to validity

Thus, I have always found interesting and intriguing, the fairly frequent discovery of prior evidence of the existence, and of the earlier recognition or descriptions in classical literature, of various concepts or clinical entities which are now well established in modern psychologic medicine. In so many areas of knowledge about human behavior, one finds that very seldom is a so-called discovery really completely new. One can accordingly and perhaps surprisingly postulate that if an observation in human psychology is to be considered as really valid, some astute observer will very likely have noted it previously in some way, perhaps even long, long ago! It may not have had a name, or it may have had quite a different one than the one current or proposed, but some astute person will have observed it. Some description is then likely to be found from the past several centuries, from the medieval era, or in the more ancient writings.

I have on occasion found it useful to employ such criteria as a kind of Historical Validation for certain "new" psychiatric concepts which I had observed and was considering reporting. As far as I was concerned consciously, my idea was original, or at the least independently arrived at. However, if it had some genuine validity and applicability, I came to expect that a thorough enough search would often eventually reveal some actual or implied earlier

34

recognition by a writer, philosopher, scholar, historian, or poet.*

Ancient philosophers or scholars may have used entirely different terms. However, in many, many instances the depth and penetration of their insight into human motivation and behavior has been unsurpassed, and modern conceptions can often be seen in the light of their being restatements or elaborations of principles long since recognized. Such recognition may have been individual or inadequately published or even barely so at the time.

(3) A research challenge

Along these lines of thought, it is difficult to say precisely when the concepts of the unconscious and of repression were introduced, although much of the credit for our present level of understanding must go to Sigmund Freud. This offers to the interested student a challenge for further research into ancient lore.

In accord with the foregoing, it would hardly be surprising for research eventually to find further evidence, indicating more recognition in antiquity. In view of the great importance of the concepts of Repression and the unconscious in human behavior and psychology, one might well make such a prediction. Some historical notes on Repression are further appropriate perhaps, because of this same level of importance which might be applied to the background of this kind of very basic and universal psychologic process.

B. VERDRÄNGUNG

The German word *Verdrängung,* or repression, likely first was employed in any sense close to our present usage by the psychologist Herbart [22] in 1824. The idea was also implied by Schopenhauer [44] in 1844, and doubtless by others both earlier and later.

Professor Jean M. Charcot, a genius of his time and a pioneer French psychopathologist, undertook significant work with hypnosis in the decades following 1870, demonstrating several levels of consciousness. He experimentally reproduced symptoms identical to the marked Somatic Conversions (Hysteria) of that day. His work and demonstrations were indeed momentous. Freud attended

---

* An example was the *King David Reaction.*[36] Another example will be seen in the following chapter on Sublimation (*Case 18, page 82*).

some of them and was impressed with ". . . this incomparably fine piece of . . . research . . . with which the psychical mechanism of an hysterical phenomenon was for the first time disclosed." [16]

Many observers at Charcot's clinics must have been aware of what Freud later [15] (1895) described as ". . . the strange state of mind in which one knows and does not know a thing at the same time." This statement describes the ability of the mind to dissociate; a phenomenon closely related to Repression.

C. BERNHEIM, JANET, AND BREUER; EARLY PIONEERS

(1) Bernheim

In the 1880s and 1890s, H. Bernheim [3] (1840–1919), professor of clinical medicine at Nancy, France, had undertaken important experiments in the use of hypnosis. He was probably the first to apply the term of neurosis to hysteria ". . . and for other reactions now labeled as the neuroses, or the psychoneuroses . . . Bernheim apparently recognized too, that acts might be devoid of conscious intent or even of conscious origin." [40]

We know that Freud was also familiar with his work, two prominent references written in 1895 being ". . . following the example of Bernheim when he awoke in his patients impressions from their somnambulistic [hypnotic] state which had ostensibly been forgotten . . . . [4]"; and ". . . I had myself seen Bernheim producing evidence that the memories of events during somnambulism are only *apparently* forgotten in the waking state and can be revived . . . ." [5]

(2) Janet

In these latter decades of the 19th Century, events were moving rapidly toward the further recognition, elaboration, and adoption of the psychologic bases of certain illnesses. Pierre Janet (1859–1947), a distinguished pupil of Charcot, finally formally introduced the important concept of dissociation. This theory of the splitting of the stream of consciousness [24,25] also helped to demonstrate the existence of a powerful body of unconscious data. *Das Unbewusste* (the unconscious) which had earlier been used (Hartmann in 1869 [20] and others) and which was introduced to psychoanalytic usage by Breuer [6] in 1895, was adopted, developed, and more firmly established as a concept by Freud.

(3) Breuer

Joseph Breuer [7,16] (1841-1925) first recognized that patients could be induced to relive painful "forgotten" (that is repressed) emotional situations from earlier past experience. He found that the recall of psychologically painful experiences from the past at times led to the surrender of Conversion (hysterical) symptoms. This was a momentous discovery in regard to the psychogenesis of these neurotic symptoms. The clinical results encouraged his further research, and helped attract Sigmund Freud to enter into a stimulating professional collaboration. The resulting professional association continued for some years, during which time it was highly productive.

In experiments with post-hypnotic suggestion, Bernheim had already discovered that patients were embarrassed when attempting to explain their behavior in the post-hypnotic state. He found that the embarrassment vanished as the patient was gradually induced to recall all the facts which had been lost to conscious recall.[31]

Breuer and Freud [16] further studied these phenomena and concluded that there was an important dynamic process operative. This was serving to actively secure the relegation of emotionally painful material from conscious awareness into the unconscious. Accordingly, they employed the term "Repression" (its first real use in its current dynamic sense), beginning in 1893, to express this meaning.*

D. THE FREUDIAN ERA . . . AND LATER

(1) The importance of repression: "the means of defense"

Subsequently, Sigmund Freud became the more active of the two associates in clinical work, further study, research, and writing. The concepts of Repression and the unconscious and their clinical application rapidly gained importance. By 1914 Freud [17] was able

---

* The interested student will find ten or more references in Breuer and Freud's *Studien über Hysteria,* first published in 1895 (New American Edition, 1957,[4]) for example, pp. 57, 116, 122, 123, 146, 157, 164, 214, 245, 285.

to write that the "theory of repression is the foundation stone on which the structure of psychoanalysis rests."

Further observations and experience about Repression, the Unconscious, and concepts of symptoms as defenses, led Freud further into the psychologic aspects of emotional illness, and farther from his early rather fence-straddling position about etiology when, as late as 1895, he was seeking a neurologic and organic basis for what he referred to accordingly as the three "actual" neuroses— hypochondriasis (hygeiaphrontis), neurasthenia, and anxiety neurosis. During this period, he was propounding psychologic theories to explain conversions (hysteria) and the obsessions.

All of these, as with all neuroses, we now know to be of psychogenic, that is, emotional origin. In the intervening years also, Repression has become an accepted major tenet in human psychology generally. As a consequence, it is hardly surprising today to come upon the concept of Repression or the term in the literature of nearly any scientific field, or even in the popular press.

Following Freud's elaboration of the concept of defense in the 1890s, he came to regard Repression as *the* means of defense. For nearly thirty years the concept of Repression was presented as the means whereby instinctual drives were controlled.

(2) Concepts broaden; anxiety leads to Repression

In 1926 in *The Problem of Anxiety* the Freudian evolution of analytic theory took two important steps; first, Freud recognized that anxiety *caused* Repression (in distinction to its being a result alone), and secondly, he readopted a broader concept of defense which included other ego techniques. In other words, Repression, a first acquaintance, became recognized as one of a number of dynamisms—of ego defenses.

Today we see Repression as an ego defense bringing about (when "successful") a thorough dismissal of intolerable emotional data from consciousness. Through it, the ego excludes areas of id drives, conflictual material, and subjectively intolerable thoughts, events, and emotions. Thus the experiencing of anger in an otherwise appropriate situation may not occur—or love, or passion, or envy, or resentment, and so on.

3. PRIMARY AND SECONDARY REPRESSION

A. PRIMARY REPRESSION

(1) A primordial defense

From our discussion thus far, it might perhaps be apparent that two major kinds of Repressions may be delineated. One is comprised of material which is largely instinctual, or the subject of infantile fantasies. Most of this never actually fully enters consciousness. I have found it convenient and useful to refer to this type of Repression as *primary*. This is in distinction from the later instances which are *secondary,* occurring as they do, in response to superego pressure.

Primary (or primal) Repressions may include material from fantasies, instinctual drives, possibly from certain very early experiences in the life of the individual, and from primordial emotional conflicts. Aspects of instinctual drives involved are predominantly aggressive or sexual. Their repression is a primordial defense. Non-awareness aids in control, spares conscious conflict, removes the threat of disapproval, punishment, or retaliation, and averts anxiety.

(2) The significance of painful and untoward events in infancy

A knowledge of primary repression has some practical importance in a number of disciplines. Undoubtedly instances of primary repression play a major role in infancy and, as such, can have a very important effect upon subsequent emotional and personality development. It is certainly a mistake to assume that the infant has no unconscious, that it contains little or nothing, or plays no significant role. It is likewise an error to believe that painful or untoward events will have no effect upon him, that "it doesn't matter, he is too little, he won't remember it anyway."

Some authorities have come to believe that the primary Repressions are the more important and vital ones. This is in accord with the views of those who hold that the roots of the major psychoses are laid down in the first twelve to eighteen months of life. Rank was particularly impressed with the events at the time of parturition. This difficult and threatening sequence of events constituted the important "birth trauma," an initial and significant area of primary (primal) Repression.

(3) Primary Repression vital to adaptation and acculturation

The areas of primary Repression are vital in the individual's processes of cultural and social adaptation. Through this primitive mechanism, the infant is never consciously aware of certain threatening instinctual drives, especially those of an erotic and aggressive nature. They have not been allowed passage from the id to the ego—and conscious awareness. Thus there is no danger of acting in response to them. Individual security is enhanced. Further, the child has been thus enabled to forgo infantile modes of relating (on the oral and anal levels) in favor of more adult and mature modes of relating. Socialization is enhanced.

The "sought after" goals of enhanced personal and social security are achieved, of course to a relative extent. When primary Repression is faulty, incomplete or exaggerated, all manner of psychopathologic phenomena can have their roots deep in this often most vital era of primary Repression. An added comment or so about this major category of Repression follows in the discussion of dynamics (pages 58–59).

B. SECONDARY REPRESSION

(1) Conscious awareness preceding loss

Under the heading of Secondary Repressions I would include material in the form of feelings, experiences, impulses, and so on which have at one time been clearly conscious. I prefer to call them secondary since (*a*) they usually occur later (that is, afterwards or secondarily) in life than the primary ones, and (*b*) they take place following (secondary to) their originally having been in conscious awareness.

It is this type of Repression which was discovered early by Breuer and Freud, Secondary Repression formed an important basis for the analytic theories developed especially by the latter. Freud considered these the more important of the two types, an evaluation which was almost unanimously held until after 1930.

(2) The more accessible and readily encountered form of Repression

Certainly the secondary type of Repression is more accessible, more encountered, and more worked with in the treatment situation. Secondary repressions more immediately underlie the com-

40

mon symptoms of emotional illness, including anxiety, conversion, and phobic symptoms. These comprised the bulk of the clinical work of the early students of dynamics. Secondary Repression takes place in response to individual (intrapsychic) needs. Its operation also receives important contributions from social pressures. Memory lapses and losses of all kinds illustrate the secondary kind of Repression.

Both types (primary and secondary) of Repression, however, are of vast importance to us for; (a) our concepts of personality development, (b) our understanding of the adaptive efforts of the organism, and (c) our therapeutic efforts. As one indication of the importance of Repression in understanding our modern concepts of psychopathology and dynamics Freud [37] once stated: "It is possible to take Repression as the center and bring all the elements of psychoanalytic theory into relation with it." Most of our discussion to follow will be concerned with secondary repressions, unless indicated otherwise.

The features about (secondary) Repression that Freud stressed early were:

(1) Repression is practically equivalent to defense.

(2) Repression allows the coexistence of knowing, and still not knowing something, at the same time.

(3) The repressed material is always unpleasant, painful, or consciously repugnant to the individual concerned. It is incompatible to the ego's consciousness and is therefore repudiated by it.

(4) The process is an automatic one, occurring completely outside the person's conscious awareness.

(5) Repression is undoubtedly of universal occurrence.

(6) "Deliberate" and "intentional" Repression implies that a motive exists, not conscious effort.

(7) What is frightening is repressed (Breuer);

also:

(8) Sexuality plays a major role in the Somatic Conversions (Hysteria) as a source of psychical trauma, and as a motive for defense, that is, for Repression.

(9) Repression of an incompatible idea takes place from the motive of defense.

41

(3) The repression of a painful experience

The following instance illustrates the early repression of a painful experience. We cannot say at what exact time this discard from consciousness took place after the event, or whether the memory loss was gradual or instantaneous and massive. From other sources the Repression appeared to have been complete at least by the age of eight years, or three years after the event. It could conceivably have been complete at nearly any given point following the terrible tragedy which took place.

Powerful motives for the Repression are apparent in the tremendous emotional feelings that must have been stimulated. This is a striking and dramatic example of the complete Repression of an entire significant experience.

Case 3
Repression of a Drowning

Helen, a five-year-old girl visiting with her family at a seashore resort, was assigned to look out for her little sister Joan, aged two years. Their mother had left them at a small play area while doing the grocery shopping. Shortly thereafter, Helen began playing with two other little girls her own age, and ignored Joan.

Joan must have wandered off by herself, across a road and down a short lane to where a bulkhead bordered the bay. Here she may have played a bit, fascinated perhaps by the water. Somehow she fell in and drowned.

This was a terrible tragedy in the family, and one which everyone tried to forget. As for Helen, she must have suffered terribly from feelings of responsibility and guilt. She never spoke of the event nor gave any sign of remembering it afterwards, an endeavor perhaps aided by a family also eager to forget.

C. MAJOR AND MINOR REPRESSIONS

Repressions cover a wide range. Ones of the magnitude of the foregoing major Repression are rare. Far more common are the reflections of minor Repressions to be found in the myriad of memory lapses in everyday living. These can be of little moment. They can occasionally be quite significant. They may betray inner feelings which we might prefer remain hidden; at other times they may be an inconvenience or a nuisance.

In acknowledgment of the wide clinical variations of the process, I would suggest that it might be quite proper to label them as major or minor. Thus there are *Major Repressions* and there are *Minor Repressions*. Such designations depend on their scope and the relative importance of the repressed material.

In the following instance, the loss of recall for parental anniversary dates was an annoying and troubling difficulty which seemed to persistently defeat the conscious efforts of the man concerned to conquer it. Such failure was a measure of the strength and tenacity of the repressing forces.

Case 4
Repression of Anniversary Dates

A 33-year-old man often gave verbal testimony to his great affection for his parents. There was no doubt that much of this was quite genuine. It might have been somewhat surprising therefore to learn of the considerable problem which he had in remembering their birthdays, anniversaries, or other special occasions. Superficially, this might have seemed even more surprising in view of the fact that his family attached more meaning to such dates than did many others. At the same time, however, this point was also a giveaway as to the significance of his problem.

Realizing that his parents were hurt by his failures and omissions in this area, this patient went to great lengths to avoid his lapses. At times he would carefully circle the appropriate days on his calendar. As a reminder he had also bought and addressed cards, having them ready to mail, only to find that he would have forgotten to mail the card, after the important date had passed. Try as he would, he seemed unable to observe these "important" dates.

He maintained for a long time during the course of his therapy that his only feelings toward and about his parents were positive ones. His struggle over their anniversaries, however, was an indication of his mixed feelings. The repression of dates important to them was a way of allowing some partially concealed expression of the hostile segment of his feelings, and aided in their continued Repression.

The study of this problem, plus several other similar ones of some moment, made his stated position of an unmixed love increasingly untenable. When he became able to more realistically face the hostile elements in his attitudes, and to more constructively cope with them, the problem he had had over the recall of anniversaries melted away.

D. ADDED CATEGORIES: PARTIAL AND TOTAL REPRESSIONS

(1) The significance of partial Repressions

One may also consider certain Repressions as (*a*) partial and, (*b*) total. The partial ones are incomplete and ineffective in so far as their intended purpose is concerned. These are of immediate importance from the standpoint of the psychic phenomena of everyday life. Psychopathologically, the partial category of Repression can lead to all manner of symptom elaboration, plus character trait development and exaggeration.

(2) Total Repressions: complete and often massive

Total Repressions and their effects can often enough be distinguished clinically. These include: (*a*) memory losses (complete or relatively so), including the usually minor phenomenon of blocking, (*b*) emotional failures, wherein the individual does not experience at all a given, and otherwise appropriate emotion (for example, love, hate, jealousy, resentment, and so on), and (*c*) certain rather absolute inhibitions and prohibitions can occur, such as in relation to various types of sexual activity, (hysterical) conversion paralyses, blindness, or other kinds of sensory deprivations.

(3) Repression as a mental mechanism and as the precursor of others

Repression is of such importance that some may prefer not to include it under the heading of the mental mechanisms. I would include it because unaided it constitutes a potent defensive operation. It is also a precursor of many, if not all, the other mental mechanisms. These come into play to enhance, to reinforce, or to protect the repression. I would consider it to be an integral part of our adaptive processes. Not only is it a major mechanism, but it is the grandfather of them all.

Repression is the basic part of most of our unconscious efforts to resolve conflicts and to escape anxiety. The most familiar form of Repression is secondary Repression, by which an unacceptable or disagreeable thought or feeling is actively (but automatically and unwittingly) expelled from consciousness.

4. SOME USEFUL CONCEPTIONS

A. THE LAW OF UNIVERSAL AFFECT

(1) The association of affect to object

In understanding Repression it is clear that some association of emotion, or affect, has taken place to the thought concerned. It is this associated emotional feeling that provides the motive force, the reason for the repression. Repression does not occur by chance. It is defensive. A memory thought or urge thus becomes assigned to the unconscious because its content is unpleasant; repugnant; consciously intolerable. It may be anxiety-provoking, threatening, painful, or frightening. Its banishment is intended to spare one the associated feelings. Thus, there is an affective (emotional) basis for every instance of Repression, every memory lapse, every time something is forgotten. One may not know what it is, but it is always present.

It is often easier to detect feelings which are unpleasant. They bother us, are troublesome. Soon one learns, however, that *everything,* however small or large, has some associated affect. It may be minimal and insignificant, as it often is, or it may be important and significant. It may be pleasant and positive, or unpleasant and negative, or a mixture of the two.

This leads us to our concept of the *Law of Universal Affect* [35] which I have formulated earlier and have found to be a personal convenience in communication and in teaching. This is the name thus assigned to the principle concerning the universal attachment of affect to every thought, person, idea, word, dream, fantasy, subject, and so on—in short, to every object. This is so regular and so much to be expected that it may accordingly be regarded as a law of the psyche, and has been so named. This conception is a vital one in our understanding of Repression, resistance, and of the many factors which influence associations in psychotherapy.

(2) Definition; major implications in memory retention or discard

The Law of Universal Affect may be defined as *the basic psychologic premise that every idea, thought, or object, no matter how minor or apparently neutral, possesses a distinct quantum of affect.* This may be so small as to be infinitesimal, but it is nonetheless present and can have an important effect upon the retention or discard from memory of an idea or word, and as to its relative ease of recall. The emotional feeling so possessed by an object; that is, associated with it, may be positive, negative, or mixed.

The kind of associated affect is of course quite important. So is the amount important, of course, although I think we have tended to overvalue this aspect and have assigned relatively too little significance to the kind. The universal operation of this important psychologic Law of Universal Affect leads us to an interesting related concept.

B. THE EMOTIONAL-OBJECT AMALGAM

From our recognition of the universal attachment of a certain quantum of affect, or emotional feeling to each and every object, has come the foregoing Law of Universal Affect. It is sometimes convenient, perhaps actually inescapable, that the two—the object, plus its inevitable emotional charge—come to be regarded together as a unit. Considering the combination thus is also useful to direct attention more specifically to the affective component. I have found this best met by the use of the descriptive term *emotional-object amalgam.* This has the further advantages of emphasizing the existence of the bond, and of pointing out the firm nature of the compound.

An Emotional-Object Amalgam may be defined as *the compound,* or *amalgam which is formed by the close association and attachment of an emotional charge and its object.*[32] This is a firm union, which ordinarily tends to continue, and is not readily broken. It is the union of affect, or the emotional significance which has become firmly attached, to its associated person, object, event, name, circumstance, and so on.

The amount of emotional charge or attachment for any given object may be highly variable for each person. It especially depends upon the presence and level of hidden symbolic significance. We can find important applications for this concept in the study of psychodynamics, as, for example, in the formation of phobias. Thus, as earlier described,[33] we may see here the detachment of an overload of anxiety (at the time of a critical attack of anxiety) with its displacement externally to a new object. The "selection" of an object is determined by various factors, but this phobic object, plus its newly bound emotional significance, constitutes an important kind of emotional-object amalgam. This is the object of the phobia, which has now become a neurotic object source of fear and dread.

C. ASSOCIATION OF AFFECT TO OBJECT, AND MEMORY

Memory tends to be much more highly selective than is usually recognized. The very minute amounts of affect which are associated with each item have a most important bearing upon what is retained, and what one is able to readily recall. With special training and observation, an individual may learn to more closely observe the tiny amounts of pleasant *versus* unpleasant connotations that places, names, terms, and ideas hold for him.

The "control" of memory is still, however, far more often than recognized, subject to the seeming "whims and vagaries" of the affect side of the emotional-object amalgam. The process of memory and retention, loss, or recall operates automatically and unconsciously so that even the trained observer can often only perceive an instance of either of these after it has taken place, and at this later time attempt to find explanatory associations.

Usually newcomers to the field of dynamic psychiatry find no great difficulty in accepting the Law of Universal Affect, or in understanding the concept of the Emotional-Object Amalgam. In themselves, they seem to the student to be fairly reasonable ideas. At this point, however, some questions are apt to be raised: How can such small amounts of attached affect have such a potent effect? If these amounts are so minute that we are not ordinarily aware of them, how could they prove so influential? I have found one useful explanation in an analogy to the science of electronics.

D. THE ELECTRONICS ANALOGY

The student or hobbyist in electronics necessarily learns to think in terms of microvolts. These are extremely minute amounts of electrical energy. They cannot, of course, be seen or felt. Indeed, they cannot even be measured by the more usual kinds of measuring devices. Their accurate measurement requires specialized precision instruments. Despite their minute strength, however, they can be very important in certain complex and delicate electronic circuits.

The most minor changes in potential, actually even in terms of a few microvolts in certain instances, can change or reverse an entire complex circuit. Thus the tiniest variations can result in the difference between the success of the function as planned, and circuit blocking or even reversals. This is a tangible physical fact which is usually accepted readily enough. Still, the involved functioning of electronic circuits is a simple matter, indeed, compared to the complexity of human emotional-psychologic-mental apparatus.

47

When we have thus clearly demonstrated for us in the science of electronics the tremendous overall functional differences which can occur in response to a few microvolts in one direction or the other, it seems hardly surprising that the energy of the small emotional content of so many of the human emotional-object amalgams can result in blocking, repression, difficulty in memory recall, and alteration of function and response.

E. THE CHEMICAL ANALOGY

Another analogy can be drawn which I have found to be useful sometimes in presenting the idea of the great influence of very small charges of affect. This is an analogy to the electrochemistry of certain solutions.

The ions of a true solution are tiny, electrically charged particles. The electric charges of the particles are quite minute. Still, this charge and its positive or negative nature has a tremendous overall effect in attracting or repelling other ions. In this chemical analogy, we readily learn how the minute plus or minus charges make possible the formation of all kinds of important chemical compounds. One could hardly discount their significance merely because of their minute quantity, or the difficulty involved in measuring them. Despite their almost infinitesimal strength, they can produce most significant effects. *Thus, it is with the small emotional charge intimately associated with every thought and idea in the emotional-object amalgam.*

The relative ease of recall and memory for any given object varies according to whether the quantum of emotion which is attached is pleasant or unpleasant. This also has most important implications as to: (*a*) the relative facility for learning something about a new "object"; (*b*) the relative individual resistance to the production of free associations in therapy in relation to a given area (or object); (*c*) the sequences and relative value secured by the many factors in our daily stream of mental activity; (*d*) all the vital emotional aspects of living.

5. REPRESSION, MEMORY, AND RECALL

A. INTO EVERY ASPECT OF LIVING

During our discussion thus far, it has become increasingly apparent that emotional factors consistently and profoundly influence Repression, memory, and recall. This is so basic to human life that it can hardly be overstressed. The faculty of memory is a most vital one. It enters into every aspect—major and minor—daily as well as long term—of our total living.

There are many minor but sometimes troubling and/or persistent lapses or blocks in our memory to be encountered in day-to-day living. The following examples are not overly involved or terribly unique in human experience.

Case 5
George Fails to Mail Letters

George M., a happily married young man, regularly forgot to mail letters. Several days later certain letters entrusted to him by his wife would be found crumpled in his pockets. These proved invariably to be letters written by his wife to his in-laws. He protested vigorously his unmixed affection and devotion for them—perhaps a bit too strongly.

This difficulty, and even more so its regularity and persistence, suggested the existence of conflictual feelings both toward his in-laws and about his wife's continuing relationship with them, later borne out through therapeutic study.

In the following instance a single but similar kind of lapse evolved from a different kind of conflict.

Case 6
A Businessman Forgets to Mail a Letter

The proprietor of a small local business had acquired a certain reputation for honesty. Honest he was indeed. However, when he felt within himself that something was due him he would sometimes take matters into his own hands in an attempt to even the score—as he saw it. This was not without conflict at times, however, with the pride he took in his honesty—the more so with the more doubt about his stand and his actions in response.

One year he believed certain tax levies and licenses were not justified. One way to secure redress was to deduct a like sum from his income taxes which he did, altering his financial reports accordingly. Six days after planning to mail in his return, on the due date, he found the letter still in his pocket. Conflicting feelings had blocked action at least temporarily, through his forgetting to mail in the forms.

Another common phenomenon is the failure to recall a name.

49

Generally unpleasant associations enter into this kind of blocking, although it is not always easy to uncover them. In the following instance there was a considerable background of disagreeable experience. It is as though the experience can be discarded, if one can discard (the name and identity of) the responsible party.

Case 7
The Name of a Former Business Associate is Forgotten

During his student days a man who later became my patient had spent a summer employed by the Geological Survey. He had been assigned to work for a young engineer who was most ambitious, driving, a hard task master, and a perfectionist. He was constantly pushing and demanding, and constantly sought to outperform his fellow engineers.

"We started early in the morning, ahead of the others, and rushed through the day's work as rapidly as possible. He seemed to be constantly after me to work faster and was irritated if I made the smallest error. It appeared to me that he expected me to know as much as and to be as efficient as he was. Working with him was unpleasant to say the least and I was more than happy to see the end of the summer!

"The following spring when I was filling out an application for another summer position, I could not recall his name, although I recalled the names of other engineers on the project with whom I had much less association. I still have a great deal of trouble when I try, even now—and mostly can't bring it to mind."

Lapses of memory are sometimes serious, often problematic and troublesome, at times embarrassing, and occasionally amusing. In the next instance the blocking of a name becomes far more personal. A student reported the following interesting personal instance in which he forgot his own name, with his analysis of some of the factors responsible.

Case 8
Forgetting One's Own Name

"I was a member of a social fraternity during my college days. I had become a member despite the strong objections of my parents. They believed college fraternities to be a waste of time, a source of bad associations and habits, and a colossal waste of money. My attitudes toward the fraternity were overshadowed by their opinion of the club as unsavory, and

I felt some very definite uncertainties about the 'rightness' of my belonging. I had not overridden their judgments without some great conflicts, and feelings of disloyalty, rebellion, 'badness,' and guilt.

"One of the important annual activities of the organization was to conduct a 'rush week' in order to get new members. This was a time when all school work was necessarily abandoned. All our efforts were turned to meeting as many of the prospective rushees as possible, and trying to favorably influence the more select candidates to join our ranks. Each day for a week from morning until late at night was spent meeting the boys and trying to convince them of the many assets of fraternity life: the healthy relationships possible, the good study habits of our group, and the economy of living that our house offered. Since I had some mixed feelings about these, I was not always the best salesman.

"One day, toward the end of the rush week, I joined a small group of candidates and started to introduce myself. Can you imagine the peculiar sensation I experienced when I found that I could not remember my own name! I started the conversation with 'How do you do—I am . . . .' I absolutely could not think of my own name! It was very embarrassing to say the least. I quickly tried to pass off my distress and confusion by offering what I am afraid were some pretty lame excuses, such as by explaining how tired I was from the rigorous activities of the week, etc.

"I believe the parental attitudes, with their accustomed great influences from my early years of life, were far more important than I had consciously realized. I knew very well that my activities were against my parents' wishes. The activities of rush week, with the adjournment of scholastic work, even bore out some of their pronouncements. There was also undoubtedly my own deep conviction that what I was doing was wrong; therefore I was 'wrong.' The manifestation of this unpleasant evaluation of myself was exhibited as a forgetting of my own name. I was so wrong indeed that for the moment I was no longer even entitled to a name, or at least to my own —the one my parents had given me!"

B. NIETZSCHE AND DARWIN

I have noted earlier that awareness of the forces of Repression has been evident to observant scholars for a long time. At various times philosophers and scientists have indicated their observations in relation to memory and the facility of recall. Jones [34] cited two interesting examples, one from Nietzsche and a second from Darwin. Nietzsche in *Jenseits von Gut und Böse* wrote: "I have done that, says my memory. I cannot have done that, says my pride, and remains inexorable. Finally—memory yields." This statement in simple terms indicates clearly his grasp of a cardinal principle in memory and in the Repression of memory.

This kind of admirable understanding is further demonstrated in the book, *The Life of Charles Darwin,* by his son, Francis. The book quotes the elder Darwin as saying, "I had during many years followed the Golden Rule, namely, that whenever a published fact, a new observation or thought came across me, which was opposed to my general results, to make a memorandum of it without fail and at once; for I had found by experience that such (contrary and thus unwelcome) facts and thoughts were far more apt to escape from memory than favorable ones."

The scientist who is sound and seeks scientific objectivity had indeed best be guided by such a premise. Anyone engaged in research is likely (and hopefully so!) to learn early the influence which wishful thinking can have upon observations and interpretations, as well as upon recollections.

C. THE CONVENIENT MEMORY AND PSYCHOLOGIC BLINDNESS

This brings us to mention another aspect of memory and forgetting which we have learned is so subject to unwitting influence by all manner of seeming advantages. I refer to the widespread phenomenon of the "convenient memory." In it one recalls what is advantageous, conveniently "forgetting" what is not.

This may be conscious or not. At times certainly the "convenience" of the loss might suggest a feigned loss of memory. This has social uses of course. One consciously or not, and to a greater or lesser extent, prefers and perhaps actively seeks to view himself, and to have others view him, in the best possible—the most favorable—light. This may extend from the slightest shading of events all the way to deliberate and major deceptions.

Recollections may be lost completely, altered, or reversed. All of this kind of endeavor is such a human and understandable activity that at least the milder instances are hardly regarded as social transgressions, and are likely to be viewed very charitably.

D. PRESERVING AN INACCURATE SELF-PICTURE

When recollections are lost, when unfavorable events are repressed, this can lead to a kind of psychologic blindness. Thus one can help to preserve a rather inaccurate self-picture. It is defensive in its aim and goal in that one thus "seems" to avoid facing inconsistency and self censure. Its new result is defeating in that one continues to be, and often enough to give, an impression to others of being something of which he really disapproves.

Such was true in the following example, in which instances of performance, which were inconsistent with standards strongly advocated for others, had apparently been successfully forgotten, or repressed. In this kind of instance, a convenient memory merged into psychologic blindness. It was "not how I do, but how I tell you to do," on a deeper, a less conscious level. It is also not far removed from the *King David Reaction.**

Case 9
Psychologic Blindness

A young professor had been thoroughly indoctrinated with the virtues and necessities of promptness throughout the years of his youth. In time he came himself to be most intolerant of lateness in others, as had been indeed both his parents before him.

The professor would quite often lecture the offending person on his tardiness, with a tone of voice and attitude which were quite condemning. He maintained a picture of himself as infallible in keeping his own engagements promptly. However, as one who often lectured, he had been known to be late himself on a number of occasions. Although his students especially remembered several such occasions quite well, which was hardly surprising under the circumstances, he apparently could not recognize or recall them. His was a convenient memory, but this was seemingly genuine.

He had forgotten something which he did not like anyway, and which was intolerable when it was applied to himself. It was not possible for him to remember a specific instance when he was later told of it. The idea of such an occurrence was so unacceptable to him that he had repressed any conscious recollection.

---

* The *King David Reaction* is an interesting defensive process through which one's secret attitudes toward consciously disowned aspects about one's self become instead consciously experienced as attitudes or feelings toward another person.

The consciously disowned attributes are automatically and unwittingly assigned *to* the other person, who becomes unrealistically liked (the positive King David Reaction) or hated (the negative King David Reaction; King David's Anger).

E. LOSS BY ASSOCIATION

The loss from ready conscious recall of a thought, a name, or a term almost invariably occurs because it carries some unpleasant connotation. The trained or reflective person can often find such an explanatory association if he approaches the problem properly and without preconception or bias. A relaxed neutral attitude fosters free association, which is the recommended approach.

Finding such a basis or reason for the loss is, of course, in accord with the principle of scientific determination, according to which every occurrence or phenomenon has an explanation or basis. This important principle applies in psychologic areas, as it does also in the physical sciences. The base or basis may or may not be found. It may be difficult or easy to do. However, one should hardly be satisfied with an explanation on the basis of simple chance alone.

Most of us have had the annoying or embarrassing experience of being unable to recall the name of a person who is actually very well known to us. In fact, this may even have been a person with whom we are in daily contact. Try as we will, the name will not present itself for recognition, even though we may at will perhaps even summon up a vivid mental picture of the person's physical characteristics. Such lapses are likely to become less frequent as one gains ability through self study to secure awareness of the reasons for the memory lapse. These "reasons," however, are often intriguing when discoverable.

The following instance is an interesting example of this phenomenon. There are some similarities to *Case 8* (page 50).

Case 10
Repression: A "Forgotten" Name

A young physician, Dr. G., was engaged in research work. He had postulated a new theory in regard to the relative roles of heredity and environmental factors in cancer of the uterus. A colleague with whom he worked side by side in this research project had once unnecessarily sharply and belligerently challenged some of Dr. G.'s premises before a formal meeting of the research council of the university. However, there was no outward evidence of any ill feeling as a consequence, and the two men went on working toward the same goal. Seemingly, they continued to be very good friends.

Several months later a group of dignitaries was being shown about the laboratory. One of the visitors knew Dr. G.

and immediately greeted him. When the latter turned to introduce his colleague, he found himself suddenly unable to recall his co-worker's name! With much embarrassment, he "explained" (actually a hurried and thin kind of rationalization) that there were several men in the laboratory who looked alike and he sometimes had trouble in keeping them straight.

Later, in a therapeutic session, when young Dr. G. began to reflect on this puzzling incident, he gradually recognized that the cause was traceable to repressed hostility and competitiveness with his friend. This had received considerable impetus at the time of the research council meeting several months earlier.

The following instance is one in which an otherwise unexplained antipathy toward a proposed variety of flowers for two corsages was discovered to have some deeper roots by association. That which was uncovered may have been of sufficient weight in and of itself to account for the feeling. One can speculate perhaps about contributions from other implications in this case as well. In any event, the conscious connection between his dislike of the rosebuds and his dislike of his mother's pet name for him was not readily accessible to conscious recall initially. Earlier partial Repression had helped to detach the affect to this extent from its original source.

Case 11
Some Further Explanation is Secured Concerning Opposition to a Variety of Flowers

At a Boy Scout Court of Honor, it had been decided that corsages were to be presented to the mothers of two boys who were scheduled to receive their Eagle Scout Awards. A small group of scouts, including the two to be honored, were discussing with their leaders what flowers the corsages should contain. Rosebuds were suggested, whereupon M.T., one of the Eagle Scouts-to-be swung around and actively opposed the suggestions. "No! No! No!", he shouted.

He was quite a bit more vigorous in his antipathy to the idea than the occasion might ordinarily seem to have demanded, so that the Scoutmaster asked what he had against rosebuds. All the boy could offer in explanation was that they were stupid, didn't look right, and that he for one wouldn't permit these flowers to be given. It made little difference one way or another to anyone else. Hence, it was decided that corsages be ordered which would be made up of different flowers and the meeting was closed.

Several weeks later, the scout leader was lunching with M.T. and the boy's mother. In the course of the conversation, the mother brought up the boy's infancy and said to M.T.: "You were my little rosebud." The teenager was immediately annoyed with his mother and asked her not to call him that. He was again somewhat strenuous in his objections.

Later, when the Scoutmaster and the boy were alone, the leader reminded the scout of the corsage incident and his seemingly inappropriate reaction. The boy related that his mother had in earlier years often called him her rosebud. He had never liked this and had always objected to being so called. At the time of the incident and until this conversation, however, the boy had not realized that his concern about the flowers for the corsages had borne any relation to his mother's pet nickname for him.

6. DYNAMICS

A. ANXIETY OR THE THREAT OF ANXIETY

(1) Anxiety outside of conscious awareness

Let us see further how the defense mechanism of Repression operates. Through the intrapsychic process of Repression, painful, disturbing, and conflictual thoughts or experiences are pushed into the unconscious. Consciously the process is effortless; there is no awareness of the "push."

The impetus in accomplishing Repression ultimately comes from anxiety, or the threat of anxiety. It is this intense psychic kind of pain which provides the motive and force for Repression.[29] Anna Freud [14] wrote that "Repression shows the ego struggle with instinctual stimuli . . . when it is successful, the ego knows nothing of it."

We have observed that various aspects about a given person may be repressed. Thompson [48] writes that those "aspects of the individual tend to be repressed which create great difficulties in the specific milieu which is important to the person." Alexander,[1] writing that Repression "is a function which excludes certain tendencies from becoming conscious," goes on to note that "it only occurs in cases in which the mere existence of a wish, irrespective of its realization, would cause unbearable conscious conflict." As an example, he mentions "hostile feelings against a benefactor" which "would tend to be repressed because they [would] destroy our good opinion of ourselves."

(2) The quality of associated affect

While entirely correct as regards notable Repressions, this inevitably raises questions as to where we might delimit the operation of Repressions. Certainly many items are lost to conscious recall where the amount of attached affect is not large, although unpleasant. This has been stressed in our concept of the emotional-object amalgam. I have myself taken the broader view, and would specifically include as Repressions the defensive loss to ready conscious recall of any data, in accord with our definitions and with our prior discussion.

Naturally there is much interest and concern with what brings Repression about. Alexander,[2] in the study of which psychic factors are responsible for Repression and how this process takes place, reports that "fear is the motive power behind all Repression. . . . This fear is by no means a rational or entirely conscious fear of external and actual danger, but an inner fear. . . . We might say that one part of the personality exhibits fear of another part, which in ordinary language is called conscience, and that Repression serves to avert this fear-reaction. . . . Those mental tendencies, wishes, longings, ideas are excluded from the conscious personality as would arouse self-condemnation if they entered consciousness, for this self-condemnation is associated with fear like that experienced in the face of real danger." This concept of fear approximately corresponds with our view of anxiety, as summarized in the earlier discussion.

Anxiety is an apprehensive tension which stems from the anticipation of danger, when the actual nature and source of the threat is consciously unknown. Anxiety is of intrapsychic origin. Fear in turn is the emotional response to a recognized and usually external threat or danger. Both anxiety and fear are accompanied by similar physiologic changes. Emotional conflict produces or threatens to produce anxiety. Repression is a major defensive and protective reaction in response. Ultimately, it is intrapsychic conflict about Repression. This is the usual sequence of events in Repression.

B. IS REPRESSION HARMFUL?

(1) The importance of Repression in both health and illness

I have already noted the universality of the process of Repression. It has also been stated that it plays a vital role in emotional health, as well as preceding all kinds of mental mechanisms, and all manner of symptoms of emotional illness. A categorical statement about the potential harm of Repression is rather difficult, since *it would appear that we can regard Repression as indispensable to both mental health and mental illness.*

Its protective function is certainly vital in many instances. At times its operation may provide an essential respite to a hard-pressed ego, allowing time for recuperation, mobilization of inner resources, and preparing for new onslaughts from one's external and internal environment. An organically oriented psychiatrist who poorly valued psychotherapy, used to like to say in an effort to belittle the work of his psychotherapist colleagues that Repression "cured" (more accurately: relieved, or provided some measure of conflict resolution for) far more patients than did psychotherapy! His statement was accurate. However, in view of the universality of the process of Repression, his goal of belittling the effectiveness of psychotherapy in this way was hardly secured.

(2) Repression, an indispensable defense

Menninger [39] is in agreement that "Repression is not necessarily harmful; in fact, it is absolutely necessary for the adult to keep in Repression certain tendencies which, when he was a child, were permissible." And here Menninger makes an important point: "The trouble is that most of us, through childhood misunderstandings, strive to repress some things which it is not necessary to repress, and, on the other hand, sometimes have difficulty in repressing what should remain repressed."

Stallworthy [46] also pointed out both advantages and disadvantages of Repression. He described Repression as useful and necessary, but of course subject to limitations. Where, under conditions of normal emotional development, undesirable thoughts would lead to anti-social action, there is, obviously, an advantage in having such desires repressed. Brierley [8] regarded Repression as an indispensable type of mental defense.

C. THE BEGINNINGS OF REPRESSION

(1) Repression retained within the unconscious

Primary Repression is most often part of the general reaction of the relatively undeveloped ego of the child, in response to certain threatening instinctual sexual and aggressive impulses. In this type of Repression the impulses are perceived and held within the framework of the unconscious. Because they are not permitted conscious perception does not mean that these impulses no longer exist.

I have indicated earlier the useful view of a requirement for continued energy to maintain existing Repressions. One cannot say how much is required by a given individual nor necessarily why massive Repressions are more successfully made or maintained by some than by others. Certainly, it has much to do with the immediate milieu, including the interpersonal, of the infant.

(2) The establishing of a pattern of censorship

Primary Repressions and the patterns so established help to determine what can happen later. This applies to the superego taking over certain roles earlier exercised by parents. It also applies to the carryover into adulthood of early patterns of coping with both aggression and sex. Alexander [1] explains that "Repression is . . . based on a kind of unconscious censorship which reacts automatically to unacceptable tendencies. . . . The Repression of the first incestuously tinged sexual strivings of the child establishes a general pattern of sexual Repression which persists in later life, so that at the re-awakening of sexuality in adolescence, there is a general timidity and inhibition. . . . The superego lacks the capacity of making finer distinctions, and represses sexuality in general, without being able to recognize that the object of striving is no longer the same as in childhood. . . .

"Repression starts with the superego's inner perception of a dynamic tension which tends to become conscious in order to induce the motor innervations for its release. If the tendency is in conflict with the code of the superego, the conscious ego rejects it from fear, which is the motive power of repression. . . . The fear felt by the ego for the superego is the signal which warns the ego to repress, and this intimidation of the ego by the superego can be considered as the continuation of the pressure which the parents brought to bear upon the child during the period of education [bringing up]."

D. IMPORTANT EFFECTS UPON CHARACTER FORMATION AND BEHAVIOR

Space permits the bare mention of the important effects which Repression exerts upon character trait formation, and also upon behavior. This will, however, help to emphasize the many important influences of this mechanism and the many interrelationships which exist between its operation and the developing psyche. Symonds,[47] who also looks upon Repression as a primitive mechanism, regards it and its effects as the basis from which the unconscious springs of behavior are actually formed.

While we may tend to think of Repression as a negative force, or as a loss, or an absence of something, the results in personality development may serve to accentuate outwardly reversed qualities, or invite attention to different ones. The outward personality cannot directly display that which is repressed.

Glover [18] has also been interested in the effects of Repression on character formation. He calls to our attention that "many persons are described as having such and such a character, as, for example, sterling, dependable, kindly, and so forth, not because they show any particular positive characteristics of this sort, but because they do *not* [italics added] show any unkindly, or tricky, or unscrupulous traits. . . . The absence of these or of other traits may well be a consequence of the activity of Repression."

7.   REPRESSION AND EMOTIONAL ILLNESS

A.   GOALS IN THERAPY

It is in the area of emotional illness that professionals in the health fields find some most important applications of Repression and its principles of operation. In every case of emotional illness—neuroses, character neuroses, and functional psychoses in the study of the psychic foundations—one will inevitably find repressed material.

The recovery of such material from the unconscious, its recognition, its acceptance, and the patient's learning to cope with it more constructively, are all very fundamental goals of dynamic psychotherapy and analysis.

B.   FAILURE OF REPRESSION LEADS TO PSYCHOPATHOLOGY

(1) The defensive needs redouble when depression threatens

Repressions are universal. They can be variously essential, helpful, useful, or at least not harmful. Repression can be excessive. It can also be handicapping and self-defeating. Repression in too great quantity—that is, when too much is demanded of the repressing forces, when too large a chunk of emotionally charged material is presented for such a digestive process—or when the repressive powers falter for various reasons and the previously repressed threatens to emerge into consciousness, then trouble ensues.

New and more pathologic mechanisms may be employed. Various symptoms of emotional illness can develop. Psychopathology develops when the threat is too great or when derepression threatens.

As noted, a certain amount of psychic energy is required to maintain unacceptable impulses and other unconscious material in a repressed state. If the need for this energy as required reaches too great a level, Repression alone may not be sufficient to keep the material in a repressed state. When this happens, other methods of coping with the hidden drives, emotional conflicts, and resulting tensions are called into play. These include various ones of the mental mechanisms or dynamisms.

(2) Other Dynamisms or symptoms mobilized as reenforcements

Thus, other intrapsychic defensive processes such as Identification, Introjection, Sublimation, Rationalization, and others, may be called upon unconsciously as reenforcements. When these devices fail, in turn, they may become pathologically exaggerated, and/or the hidden impulses may begin to make their appearance externally in the disguised and the symbolic form of the various symptoms of emotional and mental illness. The character defensive traits may be regarded in a somewhat comparable light.

In psychopathology Repression is always exaggerated, its failure has always threatened. Alexander writes, "In short, Repression is always exaggerated and involves tendencies which the conscious ego would not reject if they became conscious. This important automatic and over-severe inhibiting function of the superego appears as one of the most general causes of psychoneurotic disturbances . . . psychoneurotic symptoms are the dynamic results of unbearable tensions occasioned by the weight of exaggerated Repressions."

C. REPRESSION AND NEUROSES

(1) Repression is basic to neurotic reactions

O'Kelly and Muckler, after noting certain possible advantages for the individual in the operation of Repression, point out the handicaps that can ensue "if it results in deprivation of knowledge and insight." Anna Freud states that "there is a regular connection between hysteria (Conversion Reactions) and Repression."

According to Fenichel, Repression is "the main mechanism of hysteria. It expresses an attitude in which the objectionable thing is treated simply as if it were nonexistent." Anna Freud also reports further that Repression can lead to compromise formations and neurosis, and that in obsessional neurosis the "Repression is secured by Reaction Formation."

Repression also plays its part in the origin of obsessions, according to Hart, when the Repression of "a painful complex" results in the exaggerated development in consciousness of the exactly opposite quality. As an example, he mentions the childhood thief, who, having completely repressed this entire undesirable complex, eventually becomes in adult life an individual of exaggerated honesty. We might refer to this as Inversion; *see also* Chapter 5.

(2) Inadequate or unsuccessful Repression leading to neurosis

According to Sadler, "Neurotic persons, subconsciously guilty of culpable feelings and tendencies, build up defense reactions against them." Thus, "any unusually strong and persistent emotion may be the defense reaction to compensate for repressed feelings and impulses of the opposite sort." Alexander writes "Whereas the normal individual is able to domesticate and modify his unsocial, instinctual tendencies, the psychoneurotic [patient] remains more firmly fixated to them. The way which the neurotic [patient] chooses for the solution of his conflict between repressing and repressed non-adjusted mental forces is a substitution of fantasy for the actual realization of his wishes, though not even in fantasy can he express directly his non-adjusted tendencies, since the conscious adjusted portion of his personality denies their existence. The outcome is a disguised fantastic expression of them in psychoneurotic symptoms."

In my own work with the neuroses, I have found repression to play an important role in the psychodynamics of every case. Various symptoms of the neuroses may develop following Repression that constitute an inadequate or unsuccessful defense for many reasons. Such unsuccessful defenses leading to symptomatology include: (*a*) excessive or massive Repressions; (*b*) insufficient, partial or inadequate Repressions; and (*c*) exaggeration of supporting or supplemental mental mechanisms to a self-defeating, psychologically unconscious and pathologic level. Repression leads to neurotic symptomatology when it fails to perform its allotted task adequately.

8. CLINICAL EXAMPLES

A. EXAMPLES ARE WIDESPREAD

In accord with our premise that Repressions underlie every type and every case of emotional illness, we might take as examples any instance of symptom formation in any case of neurosis or functional psychosis, of character trait overdevelopment in any character neurosis, or of any unhealthy and unsatisfactory relationship in the myriad problems of living. Any of these, when studied carefully enough, and when successfully analyzed, would reveal significant unconscious data, the consequence of prior Repressions.

The recovery to consciousness of Secondary Repressions is common enough in the long-term practice of the experienced psychotherapist. Primary Repressions are more difficult to uncover. The therapist is more likely to deal with them by surmise, and indirectly via their effects or results. Anticipating their presence, however, and having some understanding of their purposes and operation, the therapist sometimes can help his patient make various constructive adjustments and changes, in mitigation of their unhealthy effects and influences.

In selecting examples, and ones could be offered which might also illustrate any category of emotional illness, I have chosen those instead in which Repression is a prominent feature. In *Case 3* we observed the massive Repression by a child of her little sister's tragic death, together with the surrounding circumstances. Comparable instances in adulthood are far more rare. However, events can be wiped out in later life.

B. THE REPRESSION OF SEXUAL ACTS

In the following unusual example, Repression took place in adulthood for the sexual act or acts leading to pregnancy, because of the great conflicts involved. Efforts to fill in the memory gap were unsuccessful.

Case 12
Repression of a Sexual Act

Mrs. R. S., a 33-year-old mother of two children aged nine and eleven years, consulted a general practitioner because of an enlarging abdominal tumor of "two or three months" duration. Her menstrual history was a bit vague, but when the physician casually asked about the possibility of pregnancy, she was offended. She and her husband had been separated for four years.

Examination disclosed an enlarged uterus, and the presence of fetal heart sounds confirmed the existence of a pregnancy which she asserted was impossible. There was also a relative genital hypesthesia. She insisted that she had not had sexual relations for the four years of separation.

Because of the interesting circumstances of such a complete memory loss for the initiating sexual act, a series of interviews was arranged. While supermoralistic attitudes about sex, a poor sexual adjustment in marriage, and a primitive superego were uncovered, the memory gap was maintained. She had some male friends, but could recollect nothing intimate having taken place in their relationships at any time. The hypesthesia was of relatively recent development. There were adequate emotional factors to account for the Repression, for the resulting memory loss, and for the symptom of hypesthesia on a conversion basis.

This woman's sincerity was not questioned by those who were in contact with her. The Repression was genuine and the poor woman was puzzled and troubled by her inability to explain what had occurred. In the light of her critical conscience, and her moralism, to which such a behavioral lapse was intolerable, the defensive intent of the loss of recall was, however, clear. The exchange of conscious condemnation for Repression and symptom formation, had seemed most advantageous and a "gain" to her unconsciously.

In the following similar instance of Repression, the recovery of the lost data was more successful. There were special circumstances uncovered which had helped to make the initiating act in this instance also intolerable.

Case 13
Illegitimacy and Repression of the Initiating Experience

A 16-year-old girl was found to be pregnant, but could not name the prospective father or recall any of the circumstances of the pregnancy's initiation. Her mother was puzzled, felt responsible and guilty, and was very distressed. With her encouragement, the girl entered psychotherapy.

It was small wonder that Repression had occurred. The sexual relationship proved to have taken place with her stepfather of twelve years' standing. Some six weeks later, his work had taken him on an extended trip outside the country. While technically perhaps it was not strictly incest, certainly from the emotional standpoint it had been, with all the attendant implications, and tremendous conflicts. There were great guilt feelings, fear of punishment, an aggressive kind of competitiveness with her mother, with a dread of retaliation, and so on. She had undoubtedly been both consciously and unwittingly seductive, but had not really intended for things to go so far.

The culmination, being highly pleasurable, gratifying, an enactment of forbidden fantasies, and in a sense a great triumph, was therefore all the more consciously abhorrent, threatening, dangerous, and the source of great guilt and self loathing.

It was worthy of notice that the Repression had been so effective that she had escaped any need for its further reenforcement by the pathologic exaggeration of other mechanisms or symptom formations. This is of added interest in view of the tremendous amount of preexisting emotional conflict, in addition to that acutely mobilized.

There are illustrations in the literature, of course, where the wish for, or fantasy alone of such forbidden sexual acts has led to Conversion Reactions.

C. EVENTS OF "THE NIGHT BEFORE" ARE REPRESSED

Memory is frequently enough lost in whole or in part in connection with escapades which are consciously repugnant. This particularly applies when alcohol is admixed liberally. The effects of the alcohol and emotional factors serve to reenforce each other with some persons in securing the Repression of various events of the night before. Often, too, Repression makes Denial more possible, or conversely Denial serves to reenforce the Repression.

In the following instance, the events of a night of ethylated activity were lost to recall. Some degree of memory loss is not uncommon following overindulgence.

Case 14
Ethylated Memory Loss

A 36-year-old business man was suffering the effects of a severe hangover the morning following a wild party. There had been an accident and his car was identified as the one involved. He was charged with leaving the scene and failing to report the mishap. Ordinarily a rather responsible chap, this kind of conduct was not in keeping with his usual self. Indeed, the entire evening, marked by his overdrinking, indecorous behavior, and so on, was not in line with the prior observations of a number of his friends.

His first reaction when the police appeared was to deny that there had been an accident. He recalled nothing about it and could only accept it as real when confronted with the incontrovertible facts. Initially, he could likewise recall none of the evening's events, although when these were recounted to him some clouded and faint recollections returned. These he acknowledged with some apology and shame, and with obvious reluctance. His inability to recall the actual accident continued.

D. REPRESSION OF HOSTILITY LEADS TO COLITIS

The following case [29] is a condensed version of the possible psychopathologic sequence of events in the long-term development of a severe and limiting functional disorder.

Case 15
Hostility, Repression, and Functional Colitis

During his early years, a child was subjected to a very demanding kind of toilet training that was quite devoid of tolerance or understanding. During this period of parental unreasonableness and harshness, the child reacted by the development of destructive feelings of hostility toward his parents. These feelings were primal and as such were likely never allowed even an original entrance into conscious awareness. They were intolerably threatening, and were kept submerged as part of his Primary Repressions.

Later in life the grown-up child met with further problems in living that his protective devices could not resolve in a constructively healthy manner. The repressed material first made itself known in the form of symptoms of chronic constipation. This eventually developed into more and more severe functional difficulties. The ultimate and tragically pathologic result was the onset of symptoms of a chronic ulcerative type of colitis.

E. DEREPRESSION AND THE ACUTE ANXIETY ATTACK

Repressions are mostly silent. It is when derepression threatens; when a breakthrough into conscious awareness impends, that difficulty arises. One of the most acute and severe manifestations is the Acute Anxiety Attack. This is one of the most disturbing and painful things to which man is heir.

Case 16
Repression Falters; the Acute Anxiety Attack

A 31-year-old machinist was driving home from work one evening when he suffered an Acute Anxiety Attack and came by taxi to a hospital emergency room for help.

This man had been feeling somewhat tense, but otherwise well enough upon leaving work that evening. He had first noted numbness and tingling in his legs. This was quickly followed by feeling wildly frightened and he had a sense of inpending doom.

"Something terrible was about to happen, but I didn't know what it was. . . . I couldn't stand it. I was completely panic stricken. . . ." His heart beat wildly and his breathing was labored. He was sure he was about to die. He managed to pull his car over and a policeman helped him get a cab.

Upon arrival at the hospital, he was visibly shaken. He looked the picture of panic, which he described. He was blanched, trembling, and dyspneic. His pulse and respiratory rates were increased, and his blood pressure was elevated. These readily detectable changes would have afforded ample proof to the greatest sceptic as to the acute and major functional changes which can accompany fear and anxiety.

History from several sources confirmed increasing tension and uneasiness for about two years, since his father's death. At about this time, he began working for a boss whose volatile temperament and characteristics were quite similar to his father's. The two never really got along well and the patient was constantly thinking about quitting. However, he continued to work for his boss because he "didn't want to let him down." On the day of his attack, the patient reported that they had had their first really open argument, and that he had threatened to quit.

Briefly, the difficulty had hinged upon repressed hostility toward his father and the conflicts this created. His father's death might have proved a greater crisis, if the relationship with his new boss had not served as a timely kind of replacement. Identification of boss with father took place, so that the former became a substitute and allowed continuation of a pattern of emotional reaction and relationship. The threat of an open break with the boss was symbolically also one with his father. This mobilized, recreated, and rekindled existing serious conflicts and added a new external danger as well. The conflicts had been unconscious. With their exaggeration, de-repression threatened and the Acute Anxiety Attack ensued.

F. DEREPRESSION IN THERAPY

The therapist must keep in mind the results of derepression in treatment. Making the unconscious conscious is useful in treatment, so that derepression is part of the therapeutic process. However, this must be handled judiciously and with due regard for the patient's ability to tolerate anxiety and to integrate new insights. One should encourage the patient to proceed at his best optimal pace.

When one studies the symptoms of the neuroses, one learns increasingly that symptom development is a likely consequence of partial and incomplete ("unsuccessful") Repression. Symptoms are often symbolic and disguised outward representations of unconscious conflicts, of which one aspect has usually been repressed.

There are usually several important unconscious purposes served in symptom formation. For example, when the symptom permits a partial disguised (and perhaps symbolic) external expression of an otherwise disowned wish, elements of self punishment in secret or more apparent form are also an accompanying consequence of the secret gratification.

At times factors within the treatment situation constitute a threat. These are not always easy to fathom. Sometimes they are not reported. Sometimes they cannot be, they are unconscious. At other times existing conflicts may be activated, or new ones created. Recognition of the existence of repressed material and its influence aids in the handling of these problems. Repression also can follow such conflicts. This is illustrated in the following case.

Case 17
Repression of Appointment Times

A young salesman, in his early twenties, was experiencing a good deal of anxiety in his therapy in reaction to strong but unconscious homosexual feelings toward his therapist, which were however beginning to threaten to erupt into consciousness.

At the time when this problem was quite acute, the therapist was twice forced by schedule changes to change the time and place of the patient's appointment from the usual afternoon time in his downtown office to a late evening appointment at an office in the therapist's home.

Both times the patient not only forgot the change, but was quite sure that the therapist had never mentioned it. This Repression, as proved by ample later associations, was due to the anxiety caused by the homosexual seduction which he had fantasied as being involved in going to the therapist's home in the evening.

There are many applications of our knowledge of Repression in considerations of therapy. As a primitive mechanism, it is encountered particularly in the more primitive types of neurosis, for example in Hysteria. It is perhaps also more likely to be met in a less involved and complex fashion in the emotional illnesses of the less sophisticated.

Twenty and more years ago, the recovery of repressed data was perhaps the major aim of many therapeutic endeavors. In treatment currently the major elements include:

(1) Adaptation and reorientation to life generally.

(2) Resolution of emotional conflicts.

(3) Emotional growth and maturity, and, as regards Repression more specifically:

(4) Making the unconscious conscious: that is, the recovery of repressed memories; (a) undoubtedly a consequence of successful therapy, as well as (b) facilitating its progress.

(5) The recognition, study, modification, and integration of repressed affects.

In analytic therapy techniques of free associations are employed to encourage the recovery of repressed data. Such recovery is not easy, nor readily secured. The patient cannot report what he does not know! Sometimes, however, associations bring out suggestive or leading data. Slips of the tongue can be quite significant. While space does not permit any thorough discussion, I would like to stress the significant role of dreams and their study, in ferreting out hidden conflicts and repressed motives or feelings.

Further, the analyst as an experienced participant observer can often suspect and be alert for what lies still hidden from his patient. In addition to disguised and symbolic representations of the repressed in dreams, the psychotherapist may observe evidences of otherwise hidden and repressed drives (and so forth) as reflected in current partial (or wholly) irrational behavior.

Finally, while for purposes of convenience in this exposition we isolate Repression as a mental mechanism, every therapist recognizes its role in the operation of all the mechanisms. He utilizes this clinically and in a practical sense. He knows that other mechanisms operate in conjunction; that these are called into play as reenforcements, and in helping integrate external manifestations of repressed impulses with other elements of the personality and society.

9. RELATIONS WITH OTHER MECHANISMS

Repression is basic to the operation of other mental mechanisms. In the study of each of them, one learns that a major function of each always lies in the maintenance or the reenforcement of Repression. In this regard, we are correct in viewing it as the fundamental defense mechanism of the ego.

White [49] emphasized that other mechanisms are often required mainly to complete what Repression has left undone. It accomplishes more than other mechanisms, however, since it masters powerful instinctual impulses in the face of which other defense measures alone would be quite ineffective. He looked upon Repression as at once more fundamental, more drastic, and more primitive than the rest.

Fenichel [12] remarked that "since the Repressed continues to exist in the unconscious and develops derivatives, it is never performed once and for all, but requires a constant expenditure of energy to maintain the Repression, while the Repressed constantly tries to find an outlet." Anna Freud looked upon Repression as the most efficacious of the mental mechanisms, but also as the most dangerous.

For Fenichel, Repression consists of an unconscious purposeful forgetting, or of not even becoming aware in the first place of internal impulses or of external events which, generally, represent possible temptations or punishments for, or mere allusions to, objectionable instinctual demands.

The "purposeful" exclusion of these data from consciousness through Repression is obviously intended to blunt their painful effects on the individual and the psychic pain and anxiety should he become aware of them. Further, Repression of intolerable urges and strivings is similarly intended to obviate the danger of acting overtly in response to them. However, though the repressed data is not experienced consciously, it remains effective. The ego can get rid of it best in those instances in which the process of Sublimation has further taken place and which some have referred to as "successful Repression." We shall shortly pursue the interesting mechanism of Sublimation as the next mechanism for our scrutiny, in the following chapter.

Hart [19] believes "if the mind cannot succeed with dissociations and rationalizations" as defenses against unbearable conflict, it may avoid such conflict by Repression. He writes, "in dissociation, each of the opposing complexes is permitted a place in the field of consciousness. In Repression, conflict is avoided by banishing one opponent [completely] from consciousness, and leaving the other in possession of the field." It is an endeavor on the part of the individual to remove the problem created by the offending complex by shutting it out from the field of consciousness. The conflict henceforth may not be manifest in the consciousness, but it does not therefore cease to exist. It persists in the deeper layers of the mind.

One inevitably learns about Repression in the study of any of the mental mechanisms or any of the emotional illnesses. It is a universal phenomenon in mental activity.

10. SUMMARY

Repression is an automatic forgetting. It is a major process employed by the ego to assign repugnant ideas and impulses to the unconscious, from which they are not subject to ready recall. Their dormancy here is a relative matter, since they remain energy-laden and potent. In distinction, Suppression is the conscious effort to forget, control, and restrain, in contrast to the automatic relegation of Repression. In many Repressions one is not aware that it has taken place.

The *Concept of Historical Validation* points out the likelihood of prior knowledge, or the recognition of almost any valid principle to some extent, by past or ancient scholars. Thus a "new" conception in the behavioral sciences can likely ultimately be found to have had prior recognition to some degree. To an extent then, such research may be used to validate a concept or theory. The work of Charcot, Bernheim, Janet and others paved the way for the early contributions of Josef Breuer and Sigmund Freud concerning the unconscious and Repression. Freud's continued study and writing is largely responsible for subsequent developments over several decades. Gradually he came to recognize that the basis of Repression lay in anxiety and that it was one of a number of important ego defenses.

Primary Repressions include the body of repressed data from infancy which never entered consciousness. This consists largely of instinctual material and includes infantile fantasies. Important influences from primary Repressions bear upon personality development, emotional health, and the establishment of emotional patterns for subsequent life. Rank considered birth trauma as part of the primary (primal) Repression.

Secondary Repressions follow later in time than the infantile primary ones. They take place secondary to their once being in conscious awareness. They are more frequently encountered in treatment and in living, but both primary and secondary Repressions are of great importance.

An entire complex or an actual experience may be repressed when the psychic trauma is sufficiently great. This is more common in earlier years. *Case 3* cited an instance in which the death by drowning of a younger sister was repressed by the older one, who had been assigned responsibility for looking after her. Repressions can occur for dates, names, words, phrases, meetings, various aspects of oneself or one's feelings, and a wide variety of items. There are *major* and *minor* Repressions. There are also *partial* and *total* Repressions.

Several conceptions were offered or reformulated which have been useful to the author personally and in teaching. The *Law of Universal Affect* states the basic premise that every thought, idea, word, or object possesses a quantum of affect. This is true no matter how apparently neutral or minor the object may seem. The *Emotional-Object Amalgam* is a convenient label for the unit of object plus its attached affect. It emphasizes the emotional component, the existence of the bond, and the firm nature of the compound.

In helping us understand further the importance and influence of very small amounts of attached affect, the *Electronics Analogy* compares the effects of the minute amounts of affect, to the major influences exerted by a change in electric potential of only a few microvolts in complex (but far less so than in human emotions) electronic circuits. A *Chemical Analogy* was also offered, drawing a comparison to the tiny plus or minus charges of the ions of a solution.

Minute amounts of positive or negative affect can have great influences on the relative ease and facility of memory and recall. Lapses of memory can be serious, major, and are often problematic. Minor ones are sometimes embarrassing, often troubling, and occasionally amusing. They take place with great frequency. Certainly the faculty of memory is a most vital one in human existence.

"Wishful Thinking" can play a role in memory and in Repression and is a serious possible pitfall for the unwary scientist. A *convenient memory* refers to conscious or unconscious forgetting where this is an advantage or convenience. *Psychologic Blindness* is the defensively-intended maintenance of non-awareness about some aspect of oneself, usually condemned in others. It can be very self defeating. Through Repression an inaccurate self picture can be perpetuated. Recall often proves more difficult or impossible because of the unpleasant nature of associations which are present. This was illustrated in *Cases 10* and *11*.

Repression follows anxiety or the threat of anxiety. It is protectively intended and may afford a necessary respite for a hardpressed ego. We may regard Repressions as both necessary and vital, and at the same time expect to find them in association with the operation of every mental mechanism and at the basis of every emotional illness. The most important applications of the principles of Repression are to be found in connection with the neuroses, character neuroses, psychoses, and in their treatment. Symptom development is a likely consequence of partial and incomplete Repression. A number of clinical examples were presented in which Repression was the outstanding feature. Applications to therapy were considered.

REFERENCES

1. ALEXANDER, F. (1948). *Fundamentals of Psychoanalysis.* P. 117. New York; Norton.
2. — *Ibid.,* p. 143.
3. BERNHEIM, H. (1947). *Suggestive Therapeutics.* New York; London Book Co.
4. BREUER, J., and FREUD, S. (1957). *Studies in Hysteria.* P. 268. New York; Basic Books.
5. — — *Ibid.,* p. 109.
6. — — *Ibid.,* p. 45.
7. BREUER, J., and FREUD, S. (1895). *Studien über Hysterie.* Leipzig; Autick.
8. BRIERLEY, M. (1951). *Trends in Psychoanalysis.* P. 260. London; Anglobooks.
9. BROWN, J. F. (1940). *The Psychodynamics of Abnormal Behavior.* New York; McGraw-Hill.
10. COLEMAN, J. C. (1950). *Abnormal Psychology and Modern Life.* P. 365. Chicago; Scott Foresman.
11. ENGLISH, O. S., and FINCH, S. (1954). *Introduction to Psychiatry.* New York; Norton.

12. FENICHEL, O. (1945). *The Psychoanalytic Theory of Neurosis.* P. 150. New York; Norton.
13. FREUD, A. (1946). *The Ego and the Mechanisms of Defense.* P. 53. New York; International Universities Press.
14. — *Ibid.,* Pp. 8, 117.
15. FREUD, S. (1957). "Miss Lucy R." In Breuer and Freud's *Studies in Hysteria.* P. 117. New York; Basic Books.
16. — (1950). *Collected Papers.* Vol. I. (First six papers). London; Hogarth.
17. — (1950). "On the History of the Psycho-Analytic Movement." *Collected Papers.* Vol. 1. P. 287. London; Hogarth.
18. GLOVER, E. (1944). "Pathological Character Formation." In *Psychoanalysis Today.* (Ed. Lorand, S.) P. 220. New York; International Universities Press.
19. HART, B. (1931). *The Psychology of Insanity.* Pp. 104–111, 112–129. New York; Macmillan.
20. HARTMANN, E. VON (1869). *Philosophie des Unbewussten.* P. 45. Berlin.
21. HEALY, W., BRONNER, A. F., and BOWERS, A. M. (1936). *The Structure and Meaning of Psychoanalysis.* P. 219. New York; Knopf.
22. HERBART, J. F. (1924). *Psychologie als Wissenschaft.* Königsberg.
23. HUNT, JOSEPH McV. (1944). *Personality and the Behavioral Disorders.* New York; Donald.
24. JAMES, W. (1890). *The Principles of Psychology.* Vol. 1. P. 210. New York.
25. JANET, P. (1908). *Le Sentiment de Depersonalization.* Paris.
26. KLEIN, M. (1952). *Developments in Psychoanalysis.* London; Hogarth.
27. LANDIS, C., and BOLLES, M. M. (1946). *Textbook of Abnormal Behavior.* New York; Macmillan.
28. LAUGHLIN, H. P. (1963). *The Neuroses.* 2nd Ed. Washington, D.C.; Butterworths (In preparation).
29. — (1956). *The Neuroses in Clinical Practice.* Pp. 129–137, 735. Philadelphia; Saunders.
30. — *Ibid.,* p. 139.
31. — *Ibid.,* p. 55.
32. — *Ibid.,* Pp. 23, 193, 203, 710.
33. — *Ibid.,* Pp. 193–196.
34. — *Ibid.,* p. 38.
35. — (1955). *A Psychiatric Glossary.* 5th Rev. Ed. Washington, American Psychiatric Association.
36. — (1954). "King David's Anger." *Psychoanal. Quart.,* **23,** 87.
37. MENNINGER, K. A. (1930). *The Mind in the Making.* P. 270. New York; Knopf.
38. — *Ibid.,* p. 269.
39. — *Ibid.,* p. 268–269.
40. NOYES, A. P. (1953). *Modern Clinical Psychiatry.* 4th Ed. Pp. 12–13. Philadelphia; Saunders.
41. O'KELLY, L. I., and MUCKLER, F. A. (1955). *Introduction to Psychopathology.* 2nd Ed. Englewood Cliffs; Prentice-Hall.
42. ORGEL, S. Z. (1946). *Psychiatry Today and Tomorrow.* Pp. 81, 83. New York; International Universities Press.
43. SADLER, W. S. (1953). *Practice of Psychiatry.* St. Louis; Mosby.
44. SCHOPENHAUER, A. (1844). *Die Welt als Wilk und Vorstellung.* 2nd Ed. Leipzig.
45. SLOTKIN, J. S. (1952). *Personality Development.* Pp. 346–375. New York; Harper.

46. STALLWORTHY, K. R. (1950). *A Manual of Psychiatry.* P. 26. New Zealand; Peryer.
47. SYMONDS, P. M. (1946). *The Dynamics of Human Adjustment.* P. 145. New York; Appleton-Century-Crofts.
48. THOMPSON, C. (1950). *Psychoanalysis, Evolution and Development.* P. 93. New York; Hermitage House.
49. WHITE, R. (1948). *The Abnormal Personality.* New York; Ronald.

CHAPTER 3

SUBLIMATION

*. . . the diversion of threatening or blocked drives
into constructive channels. . .*

1. THE NATURE OF SUBLIMATION

A. A DIVERSION OF DRIVES INTO APPROVED CHANNELS OF ENDEAVOR

(1) Sublimation : a constructive mechanism

Among the mental mechanisms of defense, Sublimation is the
most advanced and highly developed. In terms of social benefit,
aesthetics, and cultural achievement it is the most important. It
is the most developed of the Higher Order or less primitive group
of dynamisms. Through its operation, the energy of personally,
and/or socially intolerable impulses and drives is successfully

76

directed into consciously acceptable channels. Their direction and aim thus become deflected and redirected toward substitute goals.

Sublimation is a constructive mechanism. Through its operation, instinctual forces are more or less permanently harnessed. Sublimation contributes to character and personality development. It plays a major role in the prevention and resolution of emotional conflict, in the prevention of anxiety, and in the maintenance of emotional and mental health. Sublimation supplies an outlet for blocked or intolerable drives.

(2) The personal and social values of Sublimation

Through their Sublimation, inner drives which press for recognition which would prove intolerable, and for action which might well prove destructive, secure disguised outward expression and constructive utilization by their unconscious diversion into approved and useful pathways. In other words, Sublimation results in the deflection of intrapsychic energy into higher, non-aggressive and non-sexual activities. These are individually creative and useful. They are often of great cultural value.

Many social and professional activities of the most laudable nature represent successful Sublimations. The operation of this major mental mechanism can lead to the highest creative endeavors in art, medicine, law, teaching, architecture, business, research, politics, exploration, government, scientific achievement, philosophy, and many other diverse fields of human activity. Indeed, one would not be far wrong to assume the operation of Sublimation to some extent, simply on an empiric basis, in most instances of real application and devotion to an endeavor in life.

B. ORIGINS AND IMPLICATIONS OF THE TERM

To make sublime is to elevate, to dignify, or to ennoble. One who is sublime is prominent for nobility of character or attainment. Something sublime is exalted, lofty, free from dross and impurities, or eminent. Sublimation means to elevate, to purify, to refine, to raise on high, and to make sublime.

In its use in chemistry, the term of sublimation affords us an analogy to its employment in a psychologic sense. Herein it is a process of refinement and purification of certain substances, in which they are vaporized by heat and recondensed, thereby bringing about their separation from less vaporable impurities.

Roots for our term and concept of sublimation can be found in a Latin word of which the infinitive form is *sublimare,* meaning "to raise on high." The English word sublimation itself has been derived from the past participle form *sublimatus,** translatable as "having been raised on high."

The background and origins of the name for this mental mechanism are of interest in understanding the concept of Sublimation, the nature of the important intrapsychic endeavor which the term describes, and perhaps something of the views of those who adopted this term for application in the behavioral sciences.

For something to be elevated indicates that it must have been low or mean. Purification implies impurity and dross. Dignification or ennobling connotes the lack of these; baseness, or perhaps pettiness. Raising on high or elevating conveys the need for these, or perhaps a prior lowness of stature or character.

It is and has been most difficult, if not impossible, to divorce value judgments and moral overtones from the consideration of instinctual, aggressive, and sexual drives. Non-constructive, socially unacceptable, or culturally harmful, often readily enough become "wrong," "evil," or "bad." Adoption of this term suggests the presence of some moral views about the instinctual drives which become sublimated. From this standpoint, the adoption of another term for this important intrapsychic process, such as "rechannelization," "instinctual diversion," and so on, or some other more neutral term without any implication of moral judgment, might have offered some advantage.

C. DEFINITION

(1) The repressed drive secures expression

In Sublimation, the otherwise intolerable instinctual drive secures a disguised but welcome and constructive external expression. In its new guise it is higher, more noble, and secures utilization in a personally and socially acceptable avenue. One may observe similarities in our definition of Sublimation and its operation, to the mechanism of Conversion and its definition. Originally, Sublimation was applied as a dynamic term in the vicissitudes of the

---

* *Sublimis* the noun form is translated from the Latin as high or lofty, or the state of being high. *Sublimo,* the first person singular, can be translated, "I raise on high."

libidinal or sexual instincts. Thus, sexual energy was regarded as being sublimated into channels of aesthetic and creative endeavor.

Freud looked upon Sublimation as the healthiest method employed by the psyche in handling repressed sexual material. Use of the term "sexual" in this usage however had a far broader connotation than often assigned, and included anything pleasurable or sensual. In our current concepts there is ample justification for broadening our views of Sublimation so as to include the similar expression and utilization of any instinctual drives or repressed urges. In this fashion inner-libidinal energy becomes outwardly non-libidinal, and the energy of aggression and related drives becomes outwardly non-aggressive. A blocked ambition or goal can also lead to what is sometimes a more superficial type of Sublimation. Let us then proceed to offer a definition.

Sublimation is a *major mental mechanism operating outside of and beyond conscious awareness, through which instinctual drives which are consciously unacceptable, or are blocked and unobtainable, are diverted so as to secure their disguised external expression and utilization in channels of personal and social acceptability. In successful Sublimation the direction and aim of the repressed drives has been deflected into new pathways of creative endeavor.*[16] Through Sublimation, intrapsychic energy is usefully employed extrapsychically. The consequence is personal gain, often with additional aspects of social and cultural gain as well.

The activities and behavior that result from the operation of Sublimation are often highly useful and constructive. As we study this interesting dynamism it seems more likely that Sublimation is a universal phenomenon. Thus, it is probable that every successful individual has sublimated a portion of the energy from his instinctual drives into useful kinds of endeavor. Since the results of this mental mechanism of Sublimation are so often personally and socially constructive, we can well understand that many psychiatrists regard it as a healthful process. A healthy rechanneling and outward expression is thus secured for energy which otherwise would be denied a culturally acceptable outlet.[12, 13, 14] A colleague once declared that "love and Sublimation make the world go 'round."

(2) The diversion of aggressive and sexual drives into productive channels

Some of the foregoing finds confirmation by other writers. Allport says simply that: "Sublimation is a device by which an individual's anti-social impulses are made socially acceptable." [2] Coleman [5] finds in Sublimation, the "gratification of sexual desires in nonsexual activities that serve as a substitute." According to Brown,[4] "Sublimation is the resolution of frustrations of basic urges through the substitution of a socially acceptable goal." Orgel [21] looks upon Sublimation as "the unconscious mechanism by which infantile sexual aims for finding interest or pleasure are changed for those no longer . . . sexual . . . (but) on a socially acceptable level." Strecker writes that "the instinctual drives which produce shame and guilt in the individual are suppressed, and the energy produced by them is used to attain another object." [25]

Symonds [26] sees in Sublimation "a method of adjusting to conflicts . . ." in which the individual "finds ways that are socially acceptable for securing gratification for (his inner) desires and wishes." While these ways may not offer direct and complete satisfaction, "they aid in the individual's satisfaction with himself," since they are methods of which society in general approves.

Menninger [19] calls Sublimations "compromises of a type" that are "of value to society." Sexual instincts in our present social and cultural order, must be more or less thwarted. If this thwarting or frustration is followed by the turning of the energy into unproductive channels, the individual may develop symptoms of emotional illness. He may have a neurosis. Instead "if it is deflected into a productive channel, he is said to be sublimating." I might add that to me, these comments apply equally, of course, to aggressive drives.

2. SOME TYPES OF SUBLIMATION

A. SUBLIMATION FOLLOWING GREAT MISFORTUNE

(1) Sublimation leading to major endeavors

The analysis of men's inner motives is a most difficult matter even under the most favorable circumstances. Even in analysis or in intensive psychotherapy, where a patient's best conscious efforts are wholeheartedly enlisted to work with the therapist in seeking understanding, the mechanisms underlying behavior are often most elusive and recondite. If in this most favorable climate one finds the unraveling of motivation and defenses difficult, it is not surprising that instances of deep revelation are not too common. Still, throughout the course of history, one finds men who have been most strongly motivated in pursuing some given line of endeavor. Their goals have been pursued with a notable singleness of purpose and with a tremendous investment of energy. Undoubtedly Sublimation has entered into many historically noteworthy careers, but mostly the operation of this important mechanism in these has been subject only to surmise.

One relationship is worthy of note in the sequence of the beginning of certain of these great undertakings. In a number of instances there has been a clear relationship to prior great loss, misfortune, deprivation, persecution, or even torture and mutilation. At times the consequent endeavor represents a Compensation.[12, 13, 14] Other mechanisms may also be called into play singly or in combination. The frustration, anger, and psychic pain which results cannot, must not, indeed dare not secure any outward expression. Undoubtedly much has to be repressed. One very constructive pathway is for some of this to secure expression in sublimated form.

(2) The Concept of Historical Validation

Rarely one can find evidence of an appreciation of some of the foregoing on the part of some observant and wise scholar from the past.*

(3) Szu-Ma Chien the historian

This is illustrated in the following instance which dates back to more than 2000 years ago, in which the Chinese historian Szu-Ma Chien undertook his monumental history of ancient China following his castration by order of the Emperor. He provides us with some thoughtful comment in analysis of his motivation. He points

---

* This is in accord with the intriguing *Concept of Historical Validation*[12] as presented briefly in the foregoing chapter. According to this conception in the study of human behavior and motivation one can hypothecate that a "new" pattern, term, or concept has most likely already been noted by some observant scholar from the past. The terms and language may be different but the idea will prove to be essentially similar.

Sufficient research will uncover such an antecedent often enough, even helping thus to validate the discovery, new view or concept, historically. Rarely one might employ the *Concept of Historical Validation* as an important criteria in the assessment of an "original" concept, as was done with the *King David Reaction*.[18]

out how great loss or suffering can be followed by a pouring of energies into new and constructive channels. In this case, as in others which he cites, these led to the production of a number of famous classics in Chinese literature. We also learn through this illustration that major Sublimations can take place in adulthood. Sexual and aggressive drives with no acceptable outlet can thus be channeled into a major constructive endeavor.

Case 18
Sublimation Follows Mutilation

Szu-Ma Chien was an outstanding historian of ancient China, having been born in the 2nd century B.C. Prior to his undertaking this role, China came under attack by the Mongolians. The Chinese Emperor of the time was greatly worried and sent an army under General Lee to repel them. As nomads without towns or settlements it was difficult to combat the Mongol raiders. Although General Lee had a reputation for great competence and had destroyed thousands of the enemy, he ultimately lost his route across the Gobi Desert, and eventually was forced to surrender.

The Emperor, upon hearing of this disaster, became very angry, and undertook to punish the general by imprisoning his family. Being a good friend of General Lee, Szu-Ma Chien vigorously protested and tried to defend him. His arguments not only did not help his friend, but made this all-powerful ruler furious in turn with him. As a consequence the Emperor ordered Szu-Ma Chien to be castrated.

Szu-Ma Chien suffered deeply. He became depressed and felt deeply humiliated. This personal tragedy however led to his becoming an historian. Eventually he decided to devote his remaining years to write *Shih-Chi,* the history of China from the year 2700 B.C., which proved to be a peerless contribution to Chinese archives and literature. It was a monumental undertaking.

In the introduction to *Shih-Chi,* the author relates the following interesting account of the motives underlying this tremendous endeavor. "After I suffered from the punishment for the sake of Gen. Lee I sighed and asked myself repeatedly 'Is it my fault? Is it my fault? Now, my body has been incapacitated. What can I do?' Through the long hours of my grief I thought of King Wen who wrote the 'Book of Change' when he was imprisoned by his foe; I though of Confucius who began to write his 'Annals' when he was almost starved to death. I thought of Chu Ynen, the great poet of Kingdom

Tsu, who completed his masterpiece 'Freedom from Sorrow' when he was exiled from his country by the King; I thought of Tso Chiu who edited the 'Anecdotes' when he lost his sight; finally I thought of Sun Wu who accomplished the 'Philosophy of War' after his feet were amputated. As a whole, most of the immortal writings handed down through the generations were done by those who had suffered from profound sorrows in their life experience, and, in the struggle of saving their shattered souls, prayed for the flickering growth of Wisdom in the darkest hours. This is probably the true motivation by which I have devoted myself to the study of history. . . ."

B. SUBLIMATION AND CHARACTER TRAITS

(1) Sublimation and its major role in personality development and character development

Sublimation plays a major role in the molding of personality and in the development of specific character traits. Thus, such abilities and traits as studiousness, research ability, various kinds of curiosity, and literary interests may be determined by Sublimation.

In certain traits other mechanisms, such as Reaction Formation, can also play an important role. Resulting character formation can show the effects of several mechanisms and of compromises. An entire group of traits from the constellation comprising the Obsessive Personality can thus have their origins in partial Reaction Formation and Sublimation. These include meticulousness, preciseness, acquisitiveness, exactness, and parsimoniousness. Abraham [1] originally pointed out the origins of the traits of orderliness, frugality, and obstinacy as partly sublimated carry-overs from the era of bowel training in infancy.

(2) Identification and Sublimation

Sublimation is related to Identification, a relationship that is more readily pointed out in the type of sublimations leading to attitude development, certain vocational drives and character trait formations. In many of these the redirected aim and goal of the drive (and formation) is influenced through Identification. These effects may be gradual and subtle. They are no less important and vital. When early identifications are limited, the capacity for sublimation is restricted.

83

Thus certain influential people in early childhood (or rather certain facets or segments of them) come to serve as unwitting models. "Efforts" to identify provide ample inducement in given instances to help determine the direction of the sublimated drive. When Sublimation is successful the instinctual drive is not erased or repressed nor is the amount of energy therein altered. It is the aim and goal that is diverted and modified. Altering the object of the drive makes it acceptable, tolerable, and useful. This modification then permits the drive's discharge and satisfaction. Because the goal of the drive has been deflected and redirected the original drive apparently vanishes. Actually it is just as adequately and effectively discharged through its new outlet. This is a healthful result, in distinction from the damming up of blocked and undischarged kinds of id drives, which lead to neurotic manifestations.

(3) The finding of sublimated expression by a blocked drive

The following is an abbreviated example, in which early sexual curiosity was completely blocked in childhood years by stringent parental disapproval. The drive was strong and found an approved expression and utilization in sublimated form. The curiosity found a new and socially acceptable goal in intellectual pursuits.

Case 19
Sublimation: Sexual into Intellectual Curiosity

A 34-year-old zoologist was known for his intellectual curiosity and his detailed information in many areas. He devoted most of his time to research, deriving a particular satisfaction from making new observations, and especially from finding out the "how" and "why" of things. He was widely read, had an intimate knowledge of many subjects, and spent most of his leisure time in the library or in other similar activities devoted to "finding out."

This type of seeking for knowledge and intellectual curiosity had been a characteristic of his since early life. His mother remembered that as a young child his questions were interminable; that he was never satisfied with an answer but continued asking further questions.

On further investigation it was found that this behavior had become marked from around the age of five, shortly after his younger sister was born. In a greatly condensed formulation, what had been a powerful but absolutely forbidden sexual curiosity had become successfully sublimated into a more acceptable kind of intellectual curiosity. The latter had stood him in good stead educationally and professionally during subsequent years.

(4) Defensive reactions to psychiatric concepts

When the concept of Sublimation was introduced by psychiatrists around the turn of the century, society was still in the Victorian Era. The emphasis was on suppression and repression of all things sexual, and often even sensual. Matters pertaining to sexual or eliminative function were strictly taboo. Any open discussion was practically unthinkable. It was as though in the effort to achieve a higher cultural plane, people must ever more thoroughly divorce themselves from their instinctual drives.

In such an atmosphere it was hardly surprising that relationships of character formation to oral, anal, and genital function in infancy and early childhood were often defensively and vigorously rejected. To many these findings seemed far-fetched and absurd. To some, depending on their own conditioning, they were most revolting. The finding of roots of neuroses and emotional illness in the vicissitudes of the instincts and in resulting emotional conflict, was for some decades widely rejected.

This is far less true today, although, for instance, the conception of the Sublimation of an infantile interest in smearing into the vocation of painting or art work, urethral erotism into firefighting, or destructive infantile aggressiveness into slaughtering and meat handling, is still quite offensive to a certain segment of people. Perhaps the potential existence or the possibility of uncovering such relationships is threatening to some people in that they touch too close to their own areas of Repression, areas which seem far more safely avoided.

A more widespread defensive reaction to be expected today on the part of the general public is that of scepticism. Many physicians thus do not find the view of pathological, surgical, or obstetrical interests and talents as representing successful Sublimations particularly palatable, but are content to maintain a somewhat sceptical attitude, usually without pursuing the matter further, although more study of the subject might prove highly interesting and informative—both generally and personally!

C. VOCATIONAL SUBLIMATION

(1) Major professional and vocational commitments as Sublimations

Reference has been made to the widespread contribution of Sublimation to many vocational and professional activities. Sublimations may be responsible or contributory to varying extents. They may be so major as to account for an entire lifetime activity which might achieve almost any degree of success. They can be minor, unapparent and, as a consequence, of less moment to either individual or society. I have come to refer to this major aspect of this dynamism as *Vocational* (and avocational) *Sublimation*.

Vocational Sublimations are important personally; they are also significant in the social scheme of things.

(2) Aggression : its channeling into sports

Sports is a frequent area into which otherwise forbidden energy and drives are channeled. It is not tolerable socially and usually not consciously, to injure or destroy a rival, but sporting activities afford an acceptable avenue for competitive striving and for the sublimated expression of aggressive drives. These may be vocation or avocation. The participant may secure this directly, the spectator and fan more vicariously. In the following case it was possible to trace some of the process of Sublimation of aggressive drives into sports.

Case 20
The Rechanneling of Aggressiveness into Sports

A 36-year-old business man entered analytic treatment because of some increasing problems in his personal relationships. Some of these were based upon his largely unconscious aggressiveness. A sports fan and ex-athlete of some note, ordinary business activities, the spectator role, and occasional officiating, had not provided the same satisfactions as had his previous active participation. This had contributed to his current problems. Early aggressive drives had been successfully sublimated in his amateur, and later professional, activities in sports. His difficulties became accentuated when these avenues were closed by age and resulting decreasing ability.

During the course of therapeutic work we learned that he had long been aggressive. In early childhood he was unwelcome in a number of his little friends' homes because of destructive or hostile actions. Through the first three grades of school his conduct along these lines left something to be desired. He became involved in many arguments and fisticuffs. At around this time considerable force began to be exerted to secure a more socialized kind of behavior. This came jointly from parents, teachers, and school authorities. His interest in sports also dated from this era. He found that one could be acceptably and even laudably aggressive and competitive in sports.

This was not a conscious transition, however. It seemed a spontaneous and natural development. Although his scholastic attitudes and classroom behavior gradually improved, this was attributed to the pressure brought to bear. No connection was made as to the Sublimation of aggressiveness into sports, unless intuitively. His parents both became his good fans.

Not too surprisingly his main interests gravitated toward boxing and football. He made the football team in high school; went on to star in both sports in college. Subsequently he secured a berth in professional football, which he held for several years. His Sublimation had not really gained momentum until middle childhood but had been rather successful. The operation of this mechanism had resulted in more socially acceptable outlets for his aggressive and hostile drives. By preventing and resolving emotional conflict to this extent, he had been spared far more serious psychopathology.

Sublimation does not require unaltered or unmodified instinctual drives for its operation. Almost any repressed urge can secure sublimated expression and utilization of its energy in disguised form. Instincts are subject to all kinds of pressures, changes, modifications and to an extent, reversals. Management of instinctual forces leads to emotional conflict and to the employment of the various mental mechanisms by which they may be altered, and their expression denied, controlled, or disguised. It is with good reason therefore that we speak of the "vicissitudes of the instincts" in personality development and maturation.

(3) Sublimation : a gradual process

The Sublimation of aggressive drives is a gradual affair. Their harnessing and redirection is seldom dramatic and is not too likely to be particularly remarked upon by those around. Sublimation may occur slowly over a decade. As in the foregoing case this often begins in the so-called latent area of personality development.

The following case exhibited many similarities, and is accordingly quite abbreviated. Portions of the history were supplied or verified by independent sources.

Case 21
Sublimation of Childhood Aggression

John W. was described by an early friend from the city in which he grew up as the "neighborhood bully." In his preschool and elementary years his explosive temper and readiness to fight led a number of his contemporaries to give him a wide berth.

As the years progressed, however, his temper "subsided" and his reputation for belligerence declined. These developments coincided with an increasing participation in sports and an awakening interest in studies. By the time he was a high school senior he had acquired considerable proficiency in both and became a sought-after candidate for college. There he developed into a star halfback on the football team, made the wrestling team, and did well scholastically.

Today his adjustment is very good. He exhibits only a healthy amount of self-assertiveness and one would find his early problems difficult to suspect.

One might regard the foregoing not incorrectly as an instance of maturation, and so it is. However, the operation of Sublimation in its service was important. Herein suitable outlets were found for his aggressive tendencies by displacing their object and altering their mode of expression. Basic drives became altered and rechanneled into more suitable routes while still permitting their satisfaction. It was rather unlikely that this man's athletic abilities or scholastic prowess were ever consciously equated by his parents or teachers with unacceptable childhood aggressiveness, as exemplified by his bullying.

(4) Sexual energy diverted into work and professional activities

Sublimation was early studied almost exclusively in relation to the sexual instincts and the resulting changes and redirection of them. I shall purposely invite attention to the operation of this important dynamism in relation to other instinctual drives, thwarted ambitions, and blocked goals. In so doing, however, I do not want the reader to lose sight of the important role of Sublimation in the vicissitudes of the sexual drives.

At times the rechanneling of sexual energy takes place to an excessive extent; beyond what might seem objectively optimal. This is illustrated in the following example. The patient mobilized a tremendous amount of energy which he constructively utilized in many areas of activity. This, however, was at the cost of a normal sexual adjustment. So much of his sexual instinctive drives were sublimated that he became partially impotent.

Case 22
Overactive Sublimation of Sexual Drives

A 48-year-old business executive sought psychotherapy because of marital problems. The most striking single feature early noted about him was his tremendous energy. This he had employed with considerable success in a number of areas.

In his work he had achieved a measure of national recognition. He was the youngest member of his firm's board of directors and had headed up several civic and professional organizations. There were many added pieces of such evidence. For instance, although his time was intensely occupied he had built his own summer cottage. People would ask about him, "Where does he get such energy?" or "How can that man get so much done?" A business associate commented, "He handles the equivalent of three full time jobs!" Interestingly, the associate was unaware of several additional concurrent activities!

This man seemed barely aware of his relative sexual impotence, although this had contributed to the present marital difficulties. He was a person of quite superior adequacy, in all areas save the sexual. The supporting psychologic structure of this adjustment had led to some interesting side effects upon him character-wise, and in his attitudes and judgments of others. He expected everyone to be a "doer." Once quite tolerant, laziness had become to him a cardinal sin. His children also had to be busy. He had gradually become more demanding and less tolerant toward them.

It became increasingly clear during the course of therapeutic study that the energy of sexual drives had become sublimated, largely into work and professional activities. The need had been intrapsychic and had progressed beyond any mere optimal redirection of excess drives. As a consequence he had nearly lost his sexual adequacy. One can perhaps look at this another way. Herein sexual outlets of course do not have to be thwarted by external factors but can be most effectively blocked by intrapsychic ones.

The key to success in this man's therapy lay in securing an investment of a fair segment of his profuse libidinal energy in the work of treatment. When this was accomplished the project of his self-study began to make steady and satisfactory progress.

The above patient's wife had come to bitterly resent his work. This is hardly surprising. An astute person, she had some understanding of her husband's psyche. On one occasion she wrote, "Our sex life has become almost nil. The energy he pours into his work comes from this and that's why I've so bitterly resented it." His major professional achievements, substantial income, recognition, and what these obtained for the family were small compensation to her.

In considering the Vocational Sublimation of sexual drives we must not neglect the interesting symbolism sometimes to be encountered in the choice of occupation. Two interesting cases come to mind. One concerns an artistically inclined and very devoted stone mason who took great pride in matching stones by eye as to size, color, and shape, and filling gaps and holes with nearly perfect fit and a minimum of mortar. Another instance relates to a professional explorer and mountain climber whose increasing eagerness to achieve the summit while climbing was often a burden to his less motivated colleagues.

(5) Exhibitionism sublimated into acting

The following instance of Vocational Sublimation indicates what can happen when the mechanism is incompletely operative, affords incomplete protection in the face of psychic trauma, or breaks down under new stress. Emotional problems multiply. Symptoms of various kinds may have their onset.

Case 23
Sublimation and a Stage Career

A middle-aged actress entered therapy because of symptoms of anxiety and depression. Her professional career prior to six months or so of beginning treatment had been most successful. Subject to intermittent symptoms of an emotional nature, these had become intensified when the loss of a coveted role had closely followed the unexpectedly premature collapse of what had promised to be the long run of a stage production, in which she had had a leading role. Her symptoms had hinted at possible impending trouble for years. The loss of necessary external gratifications and resulting psychic support, plus the aforesaid blows, had taken place at a critical epoch in her own psychology. More serious symptoms developed.

During the course of long-term intensive psychotherapy the bases and motivations for her interest in the stage inevitably came under repeated scrutiny. Gradually evidence accumulated which documented the presence of strong exhibitionistic trends in her early years.

As a child she was an "obnoxious show-off." Under the pressures of parental and social disapproval these drives had gradually become partially sublimated into her growing thespian interests. As her active participation in the theater became more possible and more successful, the process of Sublimation received added impetus. By her late teen years few traces remained. Without the prolonged intensive study afforded by treatment, the early origins of her acting talent in sublimated exhibitionistic drives would not likely have been suspected.

In considering the foregoing very abbreviated case summary it will be helpful to bear in mind that not only can blocked exhibitionism be sublimated into a variety of avenues of more or less acceptable external expression, but also resulting conflicts can be dealt with intrapsychically by a variety of mechanisms or combinations.

This is true of other problems illustrating the operation of Sublimation, as well as other mechanisms. Case examples are selected as representative only, of the particular dynamism and of how it can operate.

(6) Sublimation contributing to career commitment

Sexual drives can become altered for various reasons to become homosexual in aim. These in turn may be repressed and the repressed drives sublimated. This led in the following instance to a successful career in interior decorating. The energy of the repressed homosexuality was constructively harnessed and utilized in a personally and socially approved manner. Repression had been maintained and social conflict was avoided. Some secret gratification was still secured through his occupation and the opportunity it afforded for being more among women, which to this patient had a symbolic meaning of belonging, that is, of being one of them.

Case 24
Homosexual Drives are Diverted into Interior Decorating

A.R. was a 48-year-old single business man who was first seen in consultation upon referral by an internist because of functional gastrointestinal symptoms. He had pursued a highly successful career as an interior decorator for years. This work had become for him his very basis for living, his *raison d'être*. Into it he had poured all the interest and energy which might have gone into other avenues.

History disclosed an absence of sexual activity or even any interests or inclination in this direction. Through study it was ascertained that he was by orientation latently homosexual. In other words his sexual inclinations were largely homosexual, without any overt activity, however, or even conscious knowledge of this on his part, since it had been thoroughly repressed long ago. Most of the drive had been successfully diverted into occupational channels. He derived great satisfaction from his successes, his prestige in the field, and from his close relationships with his largely female clientele. The decorator was never happier than when he was with a group of his female colleagues. Here he would carry on animated discussions at great length. Assuming a leadership position, he was not only in effect one of the group, but a particular or pre-eminent one. Some secret homosexual envy of the female position lingered and thus secured a measure of disguised gratification.

In this instance the defensive patterns were not fully explored. The principal reasons included the reasonably stable adjustment achieved, his relatively low level of interest in change, and the long standing and established nature of his defenses. The goals of therapy were limited accordingly. The Sublimation was successful enough to have practically secured a compromise solution of a very conflictual repressed drive. Consciously intolerable and subject to potential social censure, the energy of his conflictual sex drives managed to secure acceptable and constructive application.

The above type of case is not too rare. Generally this kind of vocational Sublimation is subject to psychiatric study and treatment in instances when it has not been ideally successful. Further, unconscious meanings, gratification in, and symbolism of the vocation can vary greatly. Needless to say the entrance of men into what are ordinarily regarded as women's fields or women into men's fields is not necessarily subject to an *a priori* interpretation of latent homosexuality. I can however recall instances of such Sublimation in a highly successful male cook, a male hairdresser, and a woman magazine editor.

In the following instance a prior vocational interest is reactivated.

Case 25
Sublimation and Renewed Vocational Commitment

A professionally trained woman, about 40 years old, had not been active vocationally for more than fifteen years. Since she had been married, she had been a housewife and was quite content with this.

Somewhat unexpectedly to her friends she went back to work, and in an artistic field which was rather unfamiliar to her. In her new activity she displayed unusual energy and outstanding abilities, soon achieving a position of some importance. In addition she became active in social welfare work and took a considerable interest in civic affairs. Later it was learned that her husband, twenty-five years her senior, had lost interest in the sexual side of their marriage and that their entire relationship had become more distant.

To indulge in any kind of liaison outside her marriage was quite unacceptable to her. The conscious qualities of her needs were changed by the acceptance of substitute goals which provided some symbolic, but quite socially acceptable outlets of expression. These developments took place somewhat gradually, and outside of any conscious recognition of their import at the time.

(7) The Sublimation of thwarted maternal and paternal drives

Satisfactions of a maternal nature are denied to many women. Spinsterhood, the loss of a spouse by death, separation or divorce, and barrenness for various reasons are not uncommon bases for frustrations of wishes for children. The resulting thwarted drives can secure sublimated outlets in a number of highly useful vocations. These include teaching, nursing, foster mothering, leadership in youth activities (Y.M.C.A., Scouts, religious groups, and so on), counseling, social work, and many vocations which are not far afield from motherhood.

The original and the substituted goals in Sublimation do not have to be so clearly related. Women in such a position may also enter religious orders or take up a diverse variety of occupations and professions. The choice of vocation in Sublimation is highly individual and is limited only by unconscious symbolism, associations, and needs. This offers few limits.

Undoubtedly the unconscious choice of an avenue for Sublimation is not determined by chance alone. In many instances the connections may be difficult to uncover. In many others one has not the chance. The most successful Sublimations leave no traces in conscious awareness. Special techniques of study are required, such as free association, dream analysis, and psycho-therapeutic study. Further, since successful Sublimations provide a solution to unconscious drives, these are likely to lead to greater emotional equanimity, not to treatment. The psychiatrist thus has a greater opportunity by and large to study those which are less successful, incomplete, or which for some reason falter.

In the following example, surgery ended the possibility of motherhood. It was a great blow to this woman. She successfully weathered this by the pouring of her energies into law, a field she had earlier abandoned after a year of training in order to be married. In her case the prior interest afforded a readily available outlet into which she could unconsciously divert the energy of her blocked drives. Some motivations had already been present for the earlier interest in law, in addition to which her husband was an attorney. The Sublimation got started with some inner struggle, but once begun with such a convenient channel available, it rapidly gained significance and momentum.

Case 26
Maternal Instincts are Sublimated

Anne S. was a 34-year-old lawyer who had displayed a great amount of energy and initiative in her drive to become successful. After completion of one year in law school she had earlier left in favor of marriage, to resume her legal schooling some years later. During the renewed work toward her law degree (which she did in night school) she also held a position of considerable responsibility during the day. Following completion of her work with top honors, she had been entirely devoted to the practice of law, in which she achieved a fair degree of success.

History in her case revealed that six months prior to her re-entry into law school she had developed carcinoma of the cervix and was forced to have a complete hysterectomy performed. She had been married for five years prior to the operation. It had been the great hope of both husband and wife to have a large family. Despite efforts and medical assistance, by the time of operation there were no children. The operation was the final blow to their hopes. It saved her life, but ended further pursuit of the family goal.

For a number of reasons they would not consider adoption. Her emotional health was threatened. Fortunately, however, her repressed strivings had subsequently been successfully sublimated into working long and hard in graduate school and later in her legal career.

The following example is similar.

Case 27
Sublimation of Thwarted Maternal Instincts

Mrs. C.H. has been married for some twenty years and although the marriage has been a good one from other respects, to her disappointment there have been no children. Her husband, a successful business man, is infertile and has been disinterested in seeking medical assistance with this. He has also strongly opposed adoption. Socially and financially, the couple have a most enjoyable life except for the disappointment on the wife's part in never having had a family. Outwardly this has not seemed much of a problem, her thwarted maternal instincts having found new, satisfying, and socially beneficial outlets.

Her daily schedule for years has been filled with contacts related to children. She has been a great asset to several orphanages and homes caring for children of broken homes. She spends her afternoons and some mornings teaching in these institutions, is active in Girl Scouts, and each summer takes into her home one or two children from New York City's "Fresh Air Fund."

We see in action here the diversion of this woman's drives toward motherhood, which she could not fulfill, into many absorbing activities involving children and in a manner acceptable socially and by her husband. She cannot love or care for her own children. This has been blocked. Her maternal drives have found new avenues of expression and new objects in other children, especially those who, without parents themselves, are most in need of affection, consideration, and foster mothering.

There are many similar instances to the foregoing. A case comes to mind in which a young woman lost her husband and two children in an accident. Although there was no financial need in her case, she sublimated her maternal and marital drives into becoming the very energetic and devoted organizer of an excellent kindergarten. In another instance, a widower poured his energies and interests into being both father and mother to his three children. He did not remarry nor indeed show much interest in women.

In the following instance there were also vocational consequences.

Case 28
Sublimation and Pediatrics

A 31-year-old general practitioner applied for a residency in pediatrics which he secured and completed. He had been quite successful as a generalist but, "it's just that I want to devote my time to pediatrics; that's what I like."

He was most happy in his new field, did a splendid job, and was occasionally chided by his colleagues for spoiling his patients. Actually, from their point of view this was quite correct. In a sense he was like a great foster father to many of his young patients. It had been only after reluctantly concluding that parenthood was quite unlikely that he had begun his specialization.

He had long loved children and very strongly wanted some of his own. His interest in pediatrics had grown steadily, seemingly in inverse ratio to his hopes for parenthood. This physician had successfully sublimated his love for children of his own, which were denied him, into the allied channel of medical care for those of others.

Upon reviewing the cases for this section, a colleague reported the instance of an outstanding obstetrician from another city who had been similarly childless. He likewise took an intense fatherly interest in his infants and followed many of them over the years into adulthood. Further, several of them were usually to be found as visitors in his seashore cottage in the summertime, often accompanied by a parent. His wife was a splendid partner for such endeavors, apparently quite closely sharing his feelings and having to an extent similarly sublimated her own thwarted drives into this kind of foster parenthood activity.

(8) Sublimation and increased professional drive

Sublimation does not necessarily have to occur with primal instinctual energy as its motivation. Mention has been made of modification in instinctual drives. Also the later frustration, or the blocking of previously existing channels of expression, can lead to their substitute expression in sublimated form. Further, as we observed in *Case 26,* a prior channel can be readopted. In the next case [1] a vocation did not result from Sublimation but commitment to, plus investment and application in the existing one, became greatly increased.

This was what occurred in the following example when the process of Sublimation began around the age of thirty-five years, largely in response to frustrations provided by certain traumatic environmental and situational deprivations. This does not mean that the capacity for Sublimation as the defensive pattern of reaction had not already existed, or had even perhaps been somewhat operative heretofore in hidden fashion.

Case 29
Sublimation and Accelerated Professional Success

A 46-year-old executive had displayed unusual energy and perspicacity in his climb to a position of relative eminence in his field. Upon inquiry it was learned that he had been performing at about an average, or only slightly better, level until some eight years previously. Both his work and progress, however, up to that time, had shown little which could be regarded as outstanding. His professional advance from a positional standpoint had probably been less than average.

Further study disclosed a series of increasingly serious marital difficulties which led to an involved situation in which sexual activity in marriage became no longer possible. Extramarital relations were totally unacceptable to him because of his own personal standards. In this instance, it appeared that this man had successfully sublimated the energy of his sexual drives into professional activity in a way that had proved both effective and useful.

The satisfaction from his vocational successes had provided a measure of substitutive gratification. The great involvement in his work well absorbed energy diverted from emotional channels which had become blocked for him. The end results of his Sublimation had been personally useful and socially approved.

Stated in other words, Sublimation is the outward expression of internal drives in a concealed but legitimate form. These would otherwise be regarded as illegitimate and intolerable should conscious awareness or any outward expression *per se,* be allowed. The internal drives which secure acceptable outward expression when thus redirected are usually sexual or hostile-aggressive in nature. "Where the repressed drives return in symbolic guise acceptable to conscience and consonant with external reality, Sublimation is achieved." [3]

(9) Sublimation in a surgeon

I have indicated that vocational Sublimations can take many forms and have referred to the Sublimation of aggressive, hostile, and sadistic drives in the successful surgeon. In the following instance,[16] hidden and consciously disowned aggressive impulses thus became channeled for useful and approved outward expression in the socially valuable profession of surgery. Our discussion of this type of Sublimation would hardly be ample without the inclusion of at least one very condensed such example.

Case 30
Aggressive Sadistic Impulses are Sublimated in Surgery

In his very early years an infant was observed by a number of people to possess a considerable amount of aggressiveness and hostility. This was quite evident in his later ideas, his behavior, fantasies, and in repeated incidents with playmates. There were also several episodes of cruel and sadistic treatment of pets. His reading and hobbies confirmed these trends as well.

As he grew older, he became quite interested in hobbies, first in guns, and later in knives and sharp instruments. His hostility, sadistic trends, and his aggressive trends met with overwhelming parental and social disapproval and, almost inevitably, his own. By the time he had traversed the latent state of development there appeared to be little outward trace of these drives left.

There was, however, some growing interest in the work of physicians in the field of medicine. In adult life this man eventually became a highly successful and respected surgeon. The repressed instinctual strivings had been successfully sublimated into surgical work of high caliber. The process of Sublimation had not only been successful, but had also proved highly valuable from personal, cultural, and social standpoints.

D. AVOCATIONAL SUBLIMATIONS

(1) Partial and multiple Sublimations

I have noted that Sublimations do not necessarily have to produce vocations, although most if not all great endeavors of man are the result of, or have contributions from this interesting intrapsychic process. Most of our real drive and energy ultimately stems from instinctual sources. These can be quite powerful, and when all or most of such force follows a single channel it is not surprising that it can lead to major developments, vocational achievement, and at times to some distinct cultural and social gain. These instances are far more striking and invite attention far more readily than might smaller or minor ones. Partial ones are somewhat different, in that by being successful in a limited way, the intended defensive purpose is not subserved or is only partially and incompletely so. As a consequence, such instances are more likely to secure notice socially or therapeutically.

Let me propose an analogy in which one's instinctual energy is likened to a powerful stream of water. All of it may follow a single channel with great force. However, some of it may follow side passages of varying size. These can in turn exert effects with little or no particular relation to the main stream. Such effects may or may not be important. Sublimations may be *partial*. Sublimations are not necessarily limited to a single one, but can also sometimes be *multiple*.

In analogous fashion we can regard the many less massive Sublimations which can take place in the expression and utilization of instinctual energy. Thus we can have hobbies, and many various kinds of side pursuits and interests which secure their motive power through Sublimation. For convenience I would like to propose that these many interesting and often smaller rechannelings of instinctual energy be called *Avocational Sublimations*. They are large in number and far more common than one might ordinarily think.

(2) Gardening : a major avocational Sublimation

Avocational Sublimations, however, are not necessarily limited to minor ones. We know that for some people, a supposed avocation approaches a vocation in commitment of interest, energy, and time. This is more likely true when it serves important intrapsychic needs, as illustrated in the following case. While this woman was emotionally ill, it was apparent that Sublimation had been successful in one major area and had stood her in good stead. The development of this major Avocational Sublimation may have prevented a more severe illness or a psychotic break.

99

Case 31
The Avocation of Gardening as a Major Sublimation

Mrs. R.M., a 39-year-old housewife, had entered intensive psychotherapy because of chronic anxiety. This had become a considerable handicap to her. Somatic symptoms due mainly to muscular and visceral tension had gradually increased.

This patient had one major activity which seemed to bring her satisfaction and pleasure; namely, her strong avocation of gardening. It was a real salvation for her. She hated housework, socializing disturbed her and tended to stir up anxiety. Most kinds of leisure-type activities, such as reading or watching television, were unsatisfying.

Gardening held a special place for her, particularly the planting, transplanting, weeding, and earth handling aspects of it. She was never happier nor felt better than upon emerging after a long day of hard work in her garden; face and hands grimy, clothes soiled, dirty, and soaked with perspiration. She would begin such a day with "an eager look and a sparkle in her eye" (according to her family) and end it with "great feelings of accomplishment and satisfaction" (her words).

This patient's mother had been a terribly obsessive person, insisting on the strictest cleanliness for her entire household. After the birth of our patient, her mother had become even more strict, if such a thing were possible! As an infant and into early childhood, the importance of being clean was drilled into our patient over and over again. To the mother's dismay, however, the child was extremely difficult to keep clean—perhaps harder than most children. During these early years she had seemed to enjoy playing in dirt and filth. At times it appeared that she was deliberately vexing her mother with this behavior. This conflictual situation had a great deal of dynamic significance for both.

The mother's own attitudes and her efforts were crowned with success, however. As the child had grown older, this love of dirt had completely disappeared. By the time she was seven, she was already, if anything, an overly orderly, clean child. This had gradually become an ingrained part of her character, and she remained rather obsessively clean (although not so much as mother) during her adult life, except in relation to her gardening.

Her forcibly repressed interest in dirt and dirtiness had become gradually sublimated and re-expressed in her gardening. This was a useful occupation and the one such exception which mother had, at least tacitly, approved. This Sublimation had been clearly very successful for this patient. It was intentionally not disturbed in therapy.

(3) Contributions to hobbies and side interests

Many hobbies involve collecting. Collections may be made of all kinds of things: coins, stamps, prints, rugs, antiques, bric-a-brac, clocks, gems, jewels, and books, to name a few. Many of these have hidden, that is, symbolic meanings and can also represent Sublimations. This is true of many kinds of hobbies of course. All hobbies serve in addition as absorbers of interest and energy, some or all of which may have been so diverted.

At times, in the analytic study of a patient, a hobby, its meaning and significance come under scrutiny and these often can prove to have varied aspects which are intriguing and entertaining, as in the following.

Case 32
Courting Sublimated into Fishing

A patient in intensive psychotherapy, Robert J. was an avid fisherman. Each Saturday and Sunday he was out early and stayed late, weather permitting. In the summertime he worked two or three days weekly, and spent the other days in pursuit of his "finny friends." A fair amount of time and energy was invested in his hobby, in preparing lines and lures, in studying charts and reports, and so on. He was a good fisherman and if there were any fish to be caught, he would find them.

One day some associations led to our recognition that fish were female in his view, and eventually some intriguing unconscious symbolism was uncovered. . . Bob had been quite a "ladies' man" and Romeo in his single years. His pursuit of girls in his early teen age years however never had been very successful nor a source of much satisfaction.

Soon this had changed. He became quite expert in courting. This became a most absorbing activity. Many parallels were found in the course of therapeutic study between his courting and his fishing endeavors, which were both amusing and significant. Marriage and children had brought an end to his efforts to catch girls. This absorbing activity had now become personally quite incompatible with his new status and would have met with personal, marital, and social censure. Fishing, a minor interest as a young man, had offered him an excellent channel for the sublimation of some remaining drives not fully absorbed in the marital relationship.

In fishing he could quite actively and openly seek the best, the "real beauties." There was no conflict in this! The Sublimation provided a perfectly acceptable channel both personally and socially for his libidinal energy, in such symbolic guise. There were many associations and connections uncovered over the course of time, of which the following are samples. Thus, he could eagerly compete with other fishermen for the "best catches," the "sweet ones."

There was the satisfaction of the chase, the struggles sometimes involved in landing game fish, using various enticements (lures) for the "more reluctant ones," and matching wits with the "wary ones." He could compare his exploits with others, and discuss his catches. He could even win and display trophies as evidence of his prowess. As a sidelight to other more major areas of study, this was an interesting facet and one which the patient found entertaining at times as well as intriguing.

With its analysis he did not surrender or change his hobby. It became a bit less engrossing and demanding however and thereby, if anything, more fun as a consequence.

E. SUBLIMATION IN EMOTIONAL ILLNESS

Discussion thus far has emphasized the successful Sublimations which contribute to mental health, with some note of those which are partial, insufficient, or falter and come under surveillance in therapy. We have also learned that Sublimation can solve the pressure of inner drives in one area while leaving another untouched. This leads us to the discussion of the Sublimations which are encountered in, or which can take place during emotional sickness.

Partial, ineffective, and incomplete Sublimations can contribute to the onset of an emotional illness. At times one can see that the greater effectiveness or success of this Dynamism could have been preventive, or at least partially so. The poor Sublimations, then, can be encountered in the course of an illness; can be part of the symptomatology.

Sublimations can also occur during the course of emotional and mental illness. They are possible during the stages of various categories of neurosis and psychosis. There are a number of kinds. In some of these the energy and aim of destructive drives can become rechanneled into various constructive activities.

More pronounced instances are to be found in hospitalized psychotic patients. In one such variety of Sublimation, the new interests and endeavors are correctly welcomed by staff personnel, as indicative of improvement, although not necessarily recognized by name as Sublimations.

These instances can be seen most often to take place in the improvement and recovery phases of an emotional illness in which they are generally most prominent perhaps in occasional examples of the more assertive and destructive patients. The following is an instance which illustrates such a development.

Case 33
Sublimation in a Psychotic Illness

William Z. was a 32-year-old, single patient who had suffered the recent onset of an acute psychotic illness. He had worked for some years as an accountant and had also shown considerable mechanical ability. His hospitalization was precipitated by an acute episode in which he had been busy building a boat in his sister's garage when visitors of hers arrived. For obscure reasons the interruption this afforded had markedly upset him. His reaction was most violent. He obtained a crowbar and started tearing up his sister's house! The police soon intervened and he was shortly admitted to a state mental hospital.

On the admission ward, in every way possible, and whenever he could manage it, he continued his wrecking operations. At various times he succeeded in tearing up the pool tables, the ping pong table, water fountains, bathroom equipment, and on one occasion the exercising equipment in physical therapy. He was given tranquilizers and efforts were made to interest him in individual and group therapy. Slowly these met with some success and he began to participate in ward meetings. His destructive behavior ceased.

Instead his energy now began to be channeled into more constructive avenues. This process of Sublimation gained momentum. He began making things for the ward. He prepared molds and made several dozen serviceable ceramic ash trays. His constructive work continued. Eventually, he fashioned enough metal ash trays for the whole hospital. He began to work in the hospital shops where he designed and produced a great many complicated toys for underprivileged children, including a rather remarkable mechanical dog. He did much of the mechanical work on a hospital exhibit being readied for a medical convention. He sawed the metal legs off sixty beds to make them meet specifications for use on the open wards.

He was soon promoted to an open ward himself where he remained quite active, but his work continued to be channeled

103

into useful ends. No more destructive tendencies were exhibited and ultimately with the working out of some other problems, he was discharged from the hospital with the psychotic phase of his illness in remission, to continue psychotherapy on a private outpatient basis.

F. SUBLIMATION DURING THERAPY

Sublimation is a Higher Order mechanism. It is frequently thought of in connection with, and is present in, more mature people. Therapy is an educational process of considerable depth and one which encourages emotional maturation. It is not surprising perhaps, therefore, if upon occasion one encounters evidence of Sublimations during long-term intensive psychotherapy. It should be stressed however that the more successful and durable Sublimations generally are likely to be too subtle of onset or of presence for clear delineation.

Sublimation of part of the following patient's sexual drive took place during his more than three years of treatment.

Case 34
Sublimation a Part of Maturation During Psychotherapy

A 36-year-old engineer entered therapy because of problems in his professional work and socially. The former were far more related to a lack of interest, as distinguished from a lack of ability or intelligence. The latter included several problems, among which were those which were in consequence to his very avid girl-chasing, in which he paid too little attention to social custom or to the fine sensitivities of others' feelings.

As therapy progressed he gradually developed personality traits on the more mature side. Over a period of years his strong sexual drives moderated and came within socially acceptable bounds. What had happened to all of his energy, previously allowed such relatively free expression? This had very gradually and almost imperceptibly become (unconsciously) quite thoroughly harnessed, to secure a sublimated expression in his greatly increased professional interests and work. Both personally and socially the advantages were substantial. Both problems in essence solved themselves together.

His work increased so greatly in caliber as to enhance his professional reputation. His firm came to depend upon him for the more difficult assignments. This was a far cry from his status at the beginning of his therapeutic work. Within five years he became a partner.

104

In the following instance, improvement and developing Sublimation progressed in parallel fashion.

Case 35
Sublimation Develops During Therapy

Mrs. Rebecca H. Smith had been married for seven years. Ralph Smith, her husband, was an up-and-coming successful attorney. The Smiths had unsuccessfully tried to have children for five years. Rebecca had visited several gynecologists and had been informed that there was no apparent reason that she could not bear children.

For some years this was an increasing and nearly constant source of unhappiness and frustration to Rebecca. She felt that she had failed her husband, and for this reason she suffered from anxiety, depression, and physiologic conversion symptoms. As a consequence she entered therapy.

Last year Mrs. Smith began working in a local community school which is largely for small children of working mothers. She spends each day with a group of these youngsters. Lately she has begun to feel happier and less frustrated. Although of course she still has no children of her own, as time goes on she feels that this doesn't matter quite as much as it used to. One could observe the gradual progress of redirection, diversion, and constructive investment of blocked maternal needs. Her therapy went along well, her improvement being assisted by and parallel to the developing Sublimation.

G. PERIODIC SUBLIMATION

(1) The influences of extrapsychic and intrapsychic developments

It is not correct to assume that once established, Sublimations are fixed and not subject to further changes or development. The entire process is indeed dynamic and can both influence and be influenced by other extra- and intrapsychic developments. As noted, Sublimations can be major or minor; wholistic or partial. They can also ebb and flow and may be episodic.

At times these developments can be observed to occur during the course of long-term intensive psychotherapy. This was true in the following instance in which episodes of impotence occurred three times during the therapy of a patient. During each of these one could almost clearly see the sublimated pouring of blocked sexual energy into occupational pursuits.

Case 36
Periodic Impotence and Sublimation During Therapy

A young businessman entered psychiatric treatment because of difficulties in his marital and social relationships. A major problem had been the recent onset of impotence. He was greatly concerned about this symptom, and yet also in some contradiction, in other ways displayed a disproportionate lack of concern about his resulting loss, handicap, and limitation.* Many factors proved to enter into the psychogenesis of his periods of impotence. These included introjection and sado-masochistic operations, plus identifications from earlier significant relationships. The interesting feature for our present study however, related to the evidence of a periodic type of Sublimation taking place with each period of potency loss.

With each of three periods of complete impotence a distinct reinvestment of energy took place. The major source for such energy lay in his completely blocked sexual outlets. With the onset of impotence his interest, activity, and productivity in his business increased quite significantly. Despite the fact that other mechanisms were operative, there was still a distinct quantum of instinctual drive which became sublimated in its outward expression. While he suffered in other ways during these periods, his business benefited. One interesting consequence was that his profits would rise; an intriguing bit of economic compensation for his loss!

3. DYNAMICS

A. A CHANNEL ACCEPTABLE TO SELF AND SOCIETY

(1) An advanced member of the higher order group of Dynamisms

Much of the foregoing in text and example is not only descriptive but also brings out many important elements of the dynamics of Sublimation, how and why it develops, and the psychologic results of its employment. Sublimation is an automatic and unconscious process. It is defensive and constructive. Unconscious emotional

---

* This part of his reaction was analogous to *la belle indifférence* of the Conversion Reactions.[17] This is one manifestation of what I have termed the Secondary Defense in which *the symptom, a defense in itself, is in turn* (that is, secondarily) *defended.*

conflict is averted. Instinctual drives secure acceptable utilization. Emotional health and maturity is promoted.

It is not without good reason that we refer to Sublimation as a healthful mental mechanism. Properly also, we refer to it as the most highly developed one, the most advanced of the higher order group of dynamisms. In the brief discussion to follow, we shall review and underline a few points and perhaps add one or two.

(2) The often concurrent development of Superego and Sublimation

By definition, the mechanism of Sublimation leads to aims and activities that are acceptable by society. Since the substituted aims (secured through the Sublimation) must of necessity have the acceptance of society, effective Sublimations cannot be fully accomplished until the individual has reached a sufficiently mature stage of development. He must have reached a point where he can begin to recognize what is and what is not acceptable to society, to the world around him.[16] The process of Sublimation is at a high peak of activity during the so-called "latent" period, that is, the ages from five or six to ten years.[11] Foundations for the later operation of the defense of Sublimation are also frequently laid down during this era. Further, it is during this period also that the superego elaborates more completely. Thus the development of the superego (roughly the conscience) and the establishment of individual predilections for the present or later employment of patterns of psychic defense can take place more or less together. We have also seen in several illustrations that Sublimations can begin or receive their real impetus at almost any point in later life.

In our society, rage and sex must be held in check.[30] In other words, instinctual tensions must be discharged in modified, diverted, disguised, periodic, and in other various substitute or indirect ways which are acceptable socially. Fenichel[6] regarded periodicity as important, stating that "a prerequisite for undisturbed Sublimation is the ability to discharge instinctual tensions by (their) periodic gratification." Excluded from this possibility of periodic discharge are those childhood instincts which are not changed into anything else, but are completely repressed. The individual "simply attempts to block their discharge, thereby causing them to lose connection with the remainder of the personality, and to remain unchanged in the unconscious." Fenichel also pointed out the danger of a breakthrough which can be the basis of a neurosis. Sublimation thus may act as a preventive of neurosis.

B. AN IDEAL SOLUTION

Not everyone has the same degree of ability to develop Sublimations. This internal ability or capacity is highly variable. However, the capacity of the child to develop successful Sublimations may be one index to his ability to make a mature adaptation in later life.[16]

Freud is the one who originally advanced the theory of Sublimation, and emphasized the important part it plays in the individual's adjustment to his environment. Freud came to view Sublimation as a most healthful means of coping with repressed infantile sexual material. The infant experiences drives and impulses for which he can find no suitable, safe, or acceptable expression. These impulses are repressed. In the continuing efforts of the organism at adaptation, as it is more and more exposed to environmental experiences and pressures, some of these repressed impulses lose their original libidinal or aggressive connotation. In the resulting desexualized state, or minus their aggression, and so on, they become attached to another drive which is convenient by virtue of association, hidden meaning, or symbolism. The substituted drive or channel allows a form of outward expression that is more socially acceptable, and hence more acceptable to the individual. We have seen the results of this process in prior case studies.

In general, Freud looked upon successful Sublimation as the best solution for the outward expression of the energy of unconscious, that is, repressed, instinctual drives. The energy provides the dynamic force, but in the process it has become more refined, more useful, and more acceptable to both the individual and society. Through Sublimation, discharge of the energy becomes possible in more acceptable form. Thus we see that in healthy emotional adjustment and in sound personality development, Sublimation plays a very useful and important role. It is an ideal solution for the management and constructive utilization of the instincts and their psychic force.

C. COOPERATION OF ID, EGO, AND SUPEREGO

Modification is an important route to solution of pressing inner drives which are otherwise blocked. Modification and Sublimation are key processes in allowing the healthful (and outwardly disguised) release of conflictual urges. Thompson,[19] writing of the theory of the Id, the Ego, and the Superego, graphically described the Id as ". . . a mass of seething excitement which cannot become conscious directly. Many of its forces never reach awareness but, from time to time, portions of its energy can find some expression in the Ego by becoming connected with the memory—traces of repressed experience and thus participating in the formation of symptoms; becoming distorted as in dream symbols; or by undergoing modification, chiefly as a result of the influence of the Superego, as in Sublimation." Thompson [20] continues: "Generally, according to Henry Stack Sullivan, attributes which meet with disapproval tend to be blocked out of awareness (repressed), and are not part of the self-system, except as they sometimes gain access to it, in a disguised form through Sublimation."

This is the one process in which the major divisions of the psyche come to operate in harmony. In Sublimation they come to cooperate and to act in concert. Brierley [21] wrote that ". . . in Sublimation, the repressed achieves direct, though symbolic, expression. When it is successfully established, it must use up less energy endopsychically. The success and completeness of Sublimation, its stability, etc., are infinitely variable. Insofar as it succeeds, id, ego, and superego are cooperating and are not in opposition to each other. Sublimation, symptom formation, and reaction formations of wide scope are not relatively simple activities, like Repression, but always involve the cooperation of a number of differing mechanisms. They are vicissitudes of instinct of a high degree of complexity."

D. UNDERSTANDING BY ANALOGY

(1) The preservation and utilization of psychic energy

I have found it useful in securing an understanding of the dynamics of Sublimation to use several analogies. One, to channels of a powerful stream, has been mentioned. A second is the analogy to Niagara Falls.

We must bear in mind that each unacceptable drive or impulse that undergoes Repression requires a certain amount of energy to maintain it in its repressed state. Every repressed impulse, accordingly, theoretically detracts from the total energy that is available to the individual in the ordinary external pursuits of his daily life. In this situation Sublimation has a vital role to play.

Anna Freud [22] describes Sublimation as the diverting of purely instinctual purposes to aims which society looks upon as higher, and which are therefore also more acceptable to the Ego. In this way, the energy inherent in primitive and/or unacceptable impulses becomes transferred and directed to socially useful goals.

The following is the Niagara Falls Analogy (modified from Noyes [20]) which may be of use to us in making clearer the concept of Sublimation, and its importance as a defensive mechanism.

An analogy to Niagara Falls

A million tons of water each two minutes plummets with devastating force over the American (167 feet high and 1400 feet wide), and the Canadian (158 feet high and 2950 feet wide) sides of Niagara Falls. The tremendous energy of this vast amount of falling water can be compared to the energy of the unacceptable unconscious impulse. Such a force is irresistible. The falling water inevitably also has constantly wearing and erosive effects which might be likened in turn to the potentially destructive effects of the unconscious impulses when they are simply bottled up and denied all expression or when they are not sufficiently controlled or constructively directed.

At Niagara engineers constructed great diversionary channels which directed huge streams of water (constructively) into the turbines of hydroelectric plants. A portion of the energy and the dynamic force of the falling water was thus usefully redirected and converted into electricity, to supply power to industry and for other useful purposes.

The rechanneling of the water from the Niagara River through the hydroelectric plants was an effective diverting of part of the eroding force into constructive channels. Some of the dangerous potential was thus also averted.

This is similar to the diversion of the instinctual energy of otherwise destructive impulses into socially constructive endeavors, which takes place in Sublimation. In the psychic process a far larger proportion of the energy potential may be diverted into new, constructive, and useful channels of endeavor.

E. RELATIONS TO OTHER MECHANISMS

(1) Conversion, Compensation, Reaction Formation, Identification and Substitution

Sublimation is very important, but it does not necessarily stand alone. It has definite relations which it will be valuable for us to understand, with a number of the other mental mechanisms. We early noted the similarity in definition of Sublimation and Conversion. Young [31] wrote that "Sublimation has much in common with Compensation," providing, as it does, "substitute behavior having ethical and social approval." Fenichel [18] noted that Sublimation may be intimately related to Identification. He described the dynamic process point by point: "Sublimation is characterized by (a) an inhibition of aim, (b) a desexualization, (c) a complete absorption of an instinct into its sequella, and (d) by an alteration within the ego." He saw these steps operating also "in the results of certain Identifications, as for example in the process of the formation of the Superego."

There is a close connection in their operation between Sublimation and Reaction Formation. Sublimation, however, differs from the latter, which is the more or less complete turning into an opposite direction of disowned drives and aims. Reaction Formation results in a reversal of an aim into its opposite. In Sublimation, on the other hand, there is a redirection rather than a reversal, and we find a constructive utilization of the energy of the instinctual drives. This is the essential difference.[16] In Sublimation, the drive or outlet that has been substituted is one that is beneficial and useful to society. At the same time, it releases the energy that is needed to maintain the primitive drive in a repressed state.

The following instance points out one type of possible relationship between Sublimation and Identification.

Case 37
Identification and Sublimation

A woman had grown up with a very close relationship to her physician-father and had strongly identified herself with him in many ways. Because of this she had long wanted to become a physician herself. However, she did not have sufficient scholastic ability and was unable to secure admission to medical school. Having failed in this endeavor, she then married a man who was himself planning to study medicine. She plunged herself wholeheartedly into helping her husband through his long years of preparation, and he eventually became a successful physician.

This young woman, blocked herself in her strong desires to become a physician, redirected her goals and efforts so as to become instrumental in helping her husband to achieve what she had originally wanted for herself. In this way she deflected her energy from her own blocked ambitions into helping someone else. In this way she could still share vicariously in the attainment of this goal.

In this instance Identification was prominent early with her father and later with her husband. Sublimation solved the problem of her thwarted drives. The Identification, responsible for the original ambition, also provided the later diversionary pathway and facilitated the Sublimation. The two mechanisms were closely related in their operation.

Repression and Sublimation are also closely allied. Sublimations, according to Fenichel,[7] appear after a Repression has been removed. Sublimations require an unchecked stream of libido, just as a mill-wheel needs an unimpeded and channeled flow of water. Unless Repressions have been removed, in accord with his view, there should be no unchecked stream of libido.

Insofar as in Sublimation a higher aim or one of higher cultural values is substituted for a lower, or instinctual one, it may be considered, and has been so considered by some writers, as a specific form of Substitution. A new goal is unconsciously substituted for an unacceptable one.

(2) Sublimation : the most constructive, developed, and successful of the Dynamisms

Where does Sublimation stand in relation to other mechanisms in general? As noted, the present writer considers it the most developed and the most advanced of all the intrapsychic mental mechanisms. This process is the most important and the most constructive of all the mental dynamisms because it can form such a constructive path for the permanent resolution of the various internal conflicts over certain primitive drives and impulses. Not only is the organism released from the burden of containing the unacceptable drives and holding them in check, but it can, after Sublimation, actually devote the energy that would have to be so employed, to gainful purposes in its own behalf.

Fenichel [11] writes that all "successful defenses may be placed under the heading Sublimation." While it is true that various mechanisms may be used in successful defenses, "the common factor" is the fact that "under the influence of the ego, aim or object, or both, is changed without blocking an adequate discharge" of the energy involved. "In Sublimation the original (undesirable, unsocial, unacceptable) impulse vanishes because its energy is withdrawn" in favor of the attachment of emotional feeling to its substitute. Finally, Orgel [22] considers Sublimation as a method "of solving the problem" (of inner tension and/or anxiety caused by conflict between the demands of the instinctual drives and the demands of society) "which does not involve the need for Repression. . . . Sublimation is not a process of transforming diffuse energy to be used for other purposes, but (merely) a transfer of energy from one field to another."

4. SUBLIMATION AND MENTAL HEALTH

(1) Increasingly widespread recognition of Sublimation's importance in mental health

One of our greatest interests in Sublimation arises from the part it has to play in mental health. Several references to these important relationships have been made in the foregoing discussion. Stevenson and Neal [24] go so far as to state categorically that "mental health consists of Sublimation, that is, the refining of primitive tendencies."

There is an increasingly widespread public recognition of the contribution to emotional and mental health afforded by successful Sublimation. In illustration let me cite quotes from an article in a popular Sunday supplement.[23] This provides us with an interesting final instance. Herein one sees how the response to hurt can become sublimated in work.

Case 38
Sublimation Contributes to Emotional Health

"Whereas a few years ago she could find no parts at her studio to suit her, in the wake of a broken marriage she has quickly blossomed out as Hollywood's busiest young actress. In addition, Debbie has signed a contract with Dot Records, she is turning out albums at night, and she is declining a mounting flow of television offers. Her fan mail has burgeoned to new numbers, and she has won the sympathy and admiration of people everywhere.

" 'You see,' (Debbie is quoted as saying) 'I'm still going through a period of tremendous readjustment. I don't feel bitterness or hate toward anyone. My house is open to Eddie any time he wants to come and see the children. Bitterness and hate are qualities I've just never had. I can't understand some things, why they turned out the way they did, what I did wrong, and at times I experience flashes of anger, just momentary anger, but these are born of being puzzled and not because I'm vengeful. . . .

113

" 'The older I get' (Debbie is 27) 'the more I realize that passion rules the world, not logic or intelligence. But I'm determined not to let anything but love and common sense rule *my* world. Fortunately, I'm lucky right now in that I have work to help me over the hurdles. Work makes time pass quickly, and with the passing of time all is cured.'

"Debbie Reynolds is hurt, her vanity and ego outraged, . . . She seems to be completely without rancor. . . .

" 'I wish him only happiness,' she says, proving that for an actress and a discarded wife she is a most unusual young woman of charity, good taste, and morals—with a tremendous ability to sublimate her aggressive feelings!"

In the foregoing instance, similarities to other examples will be noted. In it we see the operation of Sublimation as a response to loss and hurt. This has been recognized by a keen observer in current living.

(2) Sublimation: a preventive of serious emotional problems

Sometimes in this manner Sublimation becomes an effective defense against hostility (and resulting anxiety) which in another person might lead to depression or one of a number of other inimical psychologic manifestations.

The ego strives for gratification for its instinctual drives. According to Fenichel,[9] "Sublimations are distinguished from neurotic substitute gratifications by their desexualization; that is, the gratification of the ego is no longer an obviously instinctual one."

Sublimation has been held, by Symonds,[26] to "represent one form of cure from neurosis." He believes that "psychotherapy may benefit the neurotic patient by providing release of energy previously used to repress and prevent unacceptable impulses from finding expression. This energy then, by Sublimation, "can be used for constructive, socially approved ends." [27]

5. SUMMARY

Sublimation is a major mental mechanism through which the energy of instinctual drives and intolerable repressed material secures disguised outward expression and constructive utilization. A new outlet becomes substituted with resulting psychologic advantage. Sublimation can be major or minor, complete and successful or partial and incompletely successful. Sublimations make a major contribution to mental and emotional health. Through them there is a diversion of drives into personally and socially approved channels of endeavor.

Sublimation is likely universal in that to varying extents, everyone sublimates parts of his basic drives into more aesthetic avenues. Society gains, and cultural advantages can accrue. More noteworthy Sublimations have led to outstanding careers in practically every field of human activity.

The introduction of this concept met with considerable resistance in the Victorian Era. However, Sublimation has had some implicit recognition for a long time. Sublimation can follow great misfortune, as illustrated in *Case 18,* and likely has in the ones mentioned therein, and in other outstanding instances throughout history. In this connection the interesting *Concept of Historical Validation* was presented. Sublimation can play an important role in the formation of a number of character traits and in personality development.

Vocational Sublimations are of great importance individually and socially. Several instances were illustrated. Laudable contributions not infrequently result. Success in many occupational and professional pursuits owes its establishment to the operation of this vital intrapsychic defensive process. Sublimation can lead to a vocation, re-establish a prior one, or result in accelerated activity in one already existing.

Avocational Sublimations constitute another important group. Some of these are difficult to distinguish from vocational rechannelings in their great commitment. Many, however, are of the nature of hobbies, part-time interests, and sidelines. Often they serve a very useful or even vital purpose in individual psychology. Important Sublimations also can occur during the course of a neurosis or psychosis, more striking ones occasionally being evident in the recovery phase of a disturbed psychotic patient.

Sublimation is healthful. It is the one mechanism in which all divisions of the psyche, the Id, Ego, and Superego, work in concert. In the most successful instances one can only surmise their existence, since these lead to contentment, equanimity, happiness, and emotional health and not to the psychiatrist's office, the person who is more likely to encounter the ones which are partial, incomplete, or which tend to break down.

In Sublimation (which is the ideal process for the solution of otherwise potentially or actively destructive inner drives), a channel for outward expression is provided which is acceptable to oneself and to society. At a high level of activity from five or six to ten years of age when the superego is being actively established, Sublimation can also begin or receive its real impetus at almost any junction in one's subsequent life.

Sublimation is similar in definition to Conversion. It is close to Reaction Formation in operation but differs in scope, direction, and end results. Substitution is a requisite to its operation in that substitutive aims and goals are adopted. Sublimation is the most developed and advanced of the mental mechanisms. It plays an important role in the securing and maintenance of emotional and mental health, in personality development and in the progress of healthful maturation.

REFERENCES

1. ABRAHAM, K. (1949). Three papers (in Ernest Jones ed.) *Selected Papers in Psychoanalysis.* Pp. 137, 248, and 418. London; Hogarth Press.
2. ALLPORT, G. W. (1938). *Personality, a Psychological Interpretation.* P. 185. New York; Holt.
3. BRIERLEY, M. (1954). Personal communication.
4. BROWN, J. F. (1940). *The Psychodynamics of Abnormal Behavior.* New York; McGraw-Hill.
5. COLEMAN, J. C. (1950). *Abnormal Psychology and Modern Life.* P. 95. Chicago; Scott Forsman.
6. FENICHEL, O. (1945). *The Psychoanalytic Theory of Neurosis.* P. 143. New York; Norton.
7. *Ibid.,* p. 142.
8. *Ibid.,* p. 141.
9. *Ibid.,* p. 142.
10. FREUD, A. (1946). *The Ego and the Mechanisms of Defense.* P. 192. New York; International Universities Press.
11. JONES, E. (1948). *Papers on Psychoanalysis,* 5th ed. Pp. 16, 27. Baltimore; Williams and Wilkins.
12. LAUGHLIN, H. P. (1963). *The Neuroses,* 2nd ed. (In the press). Washington, D.C.; Butterworths.
13. — (1959). "The Mental Mechanisms." *Bull. Mont. Co. Med. Soc.,* **3,** (9).
14. — (1959). "The Mental Mechanisms: Compensation." *Bull. Mont. Co. Med. Soc.,* **3,** (10).
15. — (1959). "The Mental Mechanisms: Inversion." *Bull. Mont. Co. Med. Soc.,* **3,** (11).
16. — (1956). *The Neuroses in Clinical Practice.* Pp. 137, 557, and 739. Philadelphia; Saunders.
17. — (1956). *Ibid.,* Pp. 259, 721.
18. — (1954). "King David's Anger." *Psychoanal. Quart.,* **23,** 87.
19. MENNINGER, K. A. (1930). *The Human Mind.* P. 118. New York; Knopf.
20. NOYES, A. P. (1953). *Modern Clinical Psychiatry,* 4th ed. Pp. 48, 53. Philadelphia; Saunders.
21. ORGEL, S. Z. (1946). *Psychiatry Today and Tomorrow.* P. 88. New York; International Universities Press.

116

22. *Ibid.*, p. 88.
23. In *Parade.* (1959). Sunday magazine supplement of March 8. "Debbie Reynolds—Darling Dynamo."
24. STEVENSON, G. H., and NEAL, L. E. (1947). *Personality and Its Deviations.* P. 104. Springfield; Thomas.
25. STRECHER, E. A., EBAUGH, F. G., and EWALT, J. R. (1951). *Practical Clinical Psychiatry,* 7th ed. P. 21.
26. SYMONDS, P. M. (1946). *The Dynamics of Human Adjustment.* New York; Appleton-Century-Crofts.
27. *Ibid.*, P. 136.
28. THOMPSON, C. (1950). *Psychoanalysis, Evolution and Development.* P. 61. New York; Hermitage House.
29. *Ibid.*, p. 75-76.
30. YOUNG, K. (1952). *Personality and Problems of Adjustment.* 2nd ed. P. 121. New York; Appleton-Century-Crofts.
31. *Ibid.*, p. 120.

CHAPTER 4

IDENTIFICATION

. . . an emotional alliance . . .

1. INTRODUCTION

   A. An important mechanism defensively and in character development
   B. Many applications individually and socially
   C. Definition

2. TYPES AND USES OF IDENTIFICATION

   A. Placing oneself in another person's shoes
   B. Empathy: a form of projective identification
   C. Personal and social value
   D. Mannerisms and traits
   E. Characterologic Identification
   F. Identification with public figures; Mass Identification
   G. A major influence in learning
   H. "Bad" identifications
   I. Compathy: affective identification
   J. In advertising: the Secondary Appeal
   K. Identification in military life
   L. Group Identification
   M. Vicarious satisfactions
   N. The "Personal Yardstick" in new relationships: the identification of a new acquaintance with someone from earlier experience

3. IDENTIFICATION WITH SIGNIFICANT ADULTS

   A. Parental Identifications by the child
   B. "Like father, like son!" "Like mother, like daughter!"
   C. Imitation and Identification
   D. Emotional contagion: the compathic communication of attitudes and emotional feelings
   E. Identification and personality development
   F. Identification encouraged by parents

4. IDENTIFICATION WITH THE AGGRESSOR

   A. A defensive operation
   B. In children's games
   C. Identification, Internalization, and Projection
   D. Identification with anticipated censure
   E. Identification and Inversion; a reenforcement of Repression
   F. Prisoners of war

5. IDENTIFICATION IN EMOTIONAL ILLNESS

   A. In Depersonalization; misidentifications
   B. In Hypochondria; Overconcern With Health, or Hygeiaphrontis

118

1. INTRODUCTION

A. AN IMPORTANT MECHANISM DEFENSIVELY AND IN CHARACTER DEVELOPMENT

Identification is a major mental mechanism or dynamism. It plays a most important role in character development. It is frequently employed as a vital psychologic defensive endeavor. Through the unconscious operation of Identification one "takes over" or develops attributes or attitudes which are in various degrees like those of another significant person.

Through Identification, acceptance, love, recognition, security and ego-enhancement may be sought. In its many applications, it would be difficult to overstress its importance. It should certainly be noted that Identification is a universally employed intrapsychic operation. It belongs to the more advanced and developed group of dynamisms.

B. MANY APPLICATIONS INDIVIDUALLY AND SOCIALLY

In the following discussion I shall undertake to present briefly a few salient points concerning several types of conscious and unconscious Identification and their uses. Included will be the utilization of this mechanism through the "secondary appeal" in advertising. Its interesting place in the social phenomenon of "mass identifications," will be noted.

I shall discuss the role of Identification in learning and in personality development. We shall also see how it enters into one's appreciation of drama, books, TV, and so on. Reference will be made to the important qualities of sympathy, empathy, and compathy. These are important forms of projective and affective identification.

Let us proceed at this point then to offer a definition of this interesting process for the purposes of our discussion.

C. DEFINITION

(1) The making of oneself like another

Identification may be defined as a *mental mechanism operating outside of and beyond conscious awareness through which an individual, in varying degree, makes himself like someone else; he identifies himself with another person. This results in the unconscious taking over and transfer to oneself of various elements of another.* Such elements may include thoughts, tasks, behavior, mannerisms, reactions, attributes, or character traits and emotional feelings.

The process of identification may be conscious or unconscious. When it is conscious, it often leads to a simple form of imitation, and the modeling of oneself after an ideal. What we are primarily considering in this discussion, however, is a deeper kind of unconscious molding of oneself. It is an intrapsychic Identification *with* someone, or with a given aspect of someone—a parent, an authority, a figure, a group, a movement, an ideal, an admired or famous personage, an actor or character, an organization, or even a criminal.

More often Identification is with a "good" figure, someone who is looked up to, or with a respected group. One then unwittingly endeavors to conform to the image of the ideal, as it is perceived. Accordingly, there frequently must be Idealization before there can be (unconscious) Identification. Most instances of Identification may be viewed as being motivated by deep basic needs for acceptance, approval, and love.

Identification, however, may be made with "good" or "bad" objects. The latter, for example, may include an aggressor, a bad authority, or even a murderer, and so on.

(2) The unconscious relegation to oneself of desired attributes

This mechanism plays a major role in emotional health. Early childhood Identifications with loved objects are necessary to sound personality development, and to emotional integration. Identification, its failure or lack, as well as so-called "misidentifications" can play a vital role in emotional illness and its treatment. An understanding of this major intrapsychic process accordingly is vital to the psychotherapist and to all who are interested in human motivation and behavior. Identification is a major mental mechanism. It is a less primitive and more advanced type of internal defensive operation. It belongs to the "higher order" group of mechanisms, although (should one wish to make such a distinction) it is on the side of this group closer to the less advanced group.

Young [25] defines Identification as the putting of oneself into the thoughts and reaction system of another. This brings with it the unconscious assumption of responses that are like those of the other person. According to O'Kelly and Muckler,[18] by the process of Identification there is the adoption, mainly unconscious, of the personality, characteristics, and identity of someone, this someone generally possessing attributes that are desired or envied. Sadler,[20] too, regards it as a process whereby the person wishfully adopts the desirable characteristics, personality or identity of another.

In other words, by the mechanism of Identification, the person unconsciously relegates to himself desirable traits that he perceives in another or others. Coleman [4] defines it as an ego defense mechanism, through the use of which the person identifies himself with some other person or institution, generally of a successful or illustrious nature.

2. TYPES AND USES OF IDENTIFICATION

A. PLACING ONESELF IN ANOTHER PERSON'S SHOES

(1) The reader and viewer

The important place of Identification in our day-to-day living can be readily illustrated. In our enjoyment of books, novels, plays, radio and television programs, Identification plays a continuing and useful role.

There is considerable individual difference in the relative capacity for Identification. Variable also is the degree of commitment and of completeness from one person to another. Our capacity in general to share the experiences of others springs in large part from this ability to identify with them.

Usually the reader, listener, or observer tends to identify with the central character; the hero or heroine of a book, a TV show, a stage play, or the movie screen. Through such Identification he may immerse himself in the actions; in the story. He may to varying extents share the emotions and experiences of a character or characters. Satisfaction, success, happiness, and sadness can be vicariously experienced. What is experienced in this common type of Identification may be an emotional feeling of likeness with a character, or with a stage or screen actor.

Through this important kind of Identification, we are enabled to more nearly share the experiences of another person. In many kinds of situations, we are far better able to appreciate and to understand another person's position, to "place oneself in another's shoes," and thus to share his emotional feelings. Only through this type of Identification can one undertake to follow the Golden Rule.

(2) Identification by the actor

A capacity for Identification is vital in turn for the would-be actor. Through Identification with the character he undertakes to portray, an actor can be far more convincing in his role. In fact, his relative ability to so identify himself will often largely determine not only his success in a given role, but also his entire career success as an actor. Good casting tries to aid this by matching actor and role. This is implied also through the expressions "in character" or "out of character."

Occasionally an actor can very completely so "place himself in the shoes of" his character as to practically live the part. This is facilitated when the actor and his role are already close characterologically. It is also aided by the matching of some of the actor's unconscious impulses, wishes, and needs with those of the person whom he portrays.

For example, a young and currently most popular French actress recently portrayed the movie role of an impulsive, amorously inclined, unconventional, and semi-delinquent girl. This role was not far removed from her real self. In addition, she fitted herself so well in the part as to literally live it during the filming of the picture. Her behavior came to be much the same both on and off the sets. She climaxed her identification with the delinquent girl in the role she was portraying in the film by running off impulsively on one occasion, in unrestrained and irresponsible fashion, blocking all production, for a brief torrid affair with the leading man in the cast.

B. EMPATHY: A FORM OF PROJECTIVE IDENTIFICATION

An important form of Identification is empathy. Of relatively recent origin, this is a useful concept of a type of intellectual and projective Identification. Empathy may de defined as *an objective, detached, and intellectualized awareness and understanding of the feelings, emotions, and behavior of another person, and/or of their meaning and significance.*[14, 15]

A capacity for empathy is an essential attribute for the psychotherapist in his joint roles of participant and observer in the process of intensive psychotherapy. It is also a very useful adjunct to everyone interested in human behavior and the behavioral sciences. The individual capacity for empathic understanding of another person is widely variable.

Empathy is to be distinguished from sympathy, and from compathy. The concept of compathy will be discussed shortly, and distinctions offered.

C. PERSONAL AND SOCIAL VALUE

The mechanism of Identification is particularly significant because of its vital role in personality development. Its useful functions thereby are not surpassed. Accordingly, the personal value of this mechanism can hardly be overestimated. This is true for most, if not all, individuals.

The social values of Identification are likewise most important. Most of the social virtues involve the operation of some kind of Identification. Interest in other people, concern for their concerns, and kindly empathic attitudes and feelings involve its conscious or unconscious operation. Some degree of projective Identification is required to secure a real measure of appreciation of the other person's position.

From a social viewpoint, this mechanism can have a large variety of valuable consequences. The following is an interesting example of one of the socially useful purposes occasionally aided or made possible through the operation of Identification.

Case 39
A Social Purpose is Subserved; Identification with a Predecessor [14]

A single man fell in love with an older woman, a widow, whom he married. The new wife had borne several children by her previous husband. The foster father became greatly interested in the children, and increasingly identified quite unconsciously with their own father. He assumed many of the real father's characteristics, and came to behave like him in many ways.

Consciously and unconsciously, he strongly desired to be like him and to take his place. As a consequence, he succeeded most admirably in his role as a foster parent. He thus came nearer to actually replacing the father.

D. MANNERISMS AND TRAITS

(1) Conscious or partly conscious adoption and its merging into characterologic change

In the foregoing example, the foster father unconsciously assumed some of the behavior of his predecessor through the mechanism of Identification. This included several of the real father's mannerisms. The small boy may "ape" an adult, especially one whom he admires or one who makes an impression. The grown-up walk or facial expressions may be copied, this being a very deliberate imitative kind of activity. Often it is seen as an outward behavioral expression of "I want to be like him!" At times it is also a way of poking fun or may constitute a form of mockery.

Imitative conscious identification differs mainly in the quality of voluntary control, assumption, and discard, as well as degree, from the Identification which takes place outside of conscious awareness. The latter may be thought of as a kind of progression in complexity, depth, and completeness of the process. Indeed, instances exist in which the conscious and effortful adoption of traits take place, which are continued, and thence what transpires is the gradual loss of awareness that the trait has been so adopted. In other words, what was deliberate adoption in the first place gradually merges into characterologic change.

(2) Admiration leading to trait adoption

Admiration and envy of status or position can contribute to mannerism and trait adoption through Identification. This took place in the following instance.

124

Case 40
A Mannerism Adopted through Identification

C. M. was a short, stocky, and somewhat awkward 13-year-old, a schoolteacher's daughter, whose parents frequently reprimanded her for the appearance of a nasal twang in her speech. She usually defended herself against these criticisms by denying its presence, or by saying she couldn't help the way she talked.

C. M.'s best friend, whom she greatly admired and whose position she envied greatly, was almost her exact opposite. She was the tall, slender, poised, and considerably pampered daughter of a leading business man. Her home, clothing, and other possessions were smarter and more expensive than those of Carol. The friend sometimes jibed Carol about her contrasting physical appearance. She possessed a marked nasal speech component.

Carol, in an attempt perhaps to win her friend's admiration, but more importantly to be like her, had unconsciously borrowed from her the one thing which could be duplicated— the nasal twang. After the girls began attending different high schools, this adopted mannerism was gradually lost.

Variations in kind and in extent of the foregoing example are encountered frequently in social and professional experience. In marked instances, mannerisms and traits can be reproduced singly or in multiple fashion. They may be continued temporarily, semi-permanently, or permanently. As Allport [2] notes, Identification can lead to the development of such close ties with another person that an individual may act as if he *was* the other. The other's characteristics are reproduced consciously or unconsciously.

(3) Contributions in symptom determination

The kind of development illustrated in Case 40 can in more marked fashion sometimes contribute to the development of serious symptoms of emotional illness. Thus, in symptoms of Somatic Conversions (Hysteria) the location and type of functional disturbance may be determined in this fashion. I reported a case earlier [13] in which a Marine Corps officer developed a "drum major gait" in which he could not bend his knees on walking. The illness was precipitated as a consequence of intolerable military stress, plus serious marital conflicts. Predisposing factors included a typical hysterical personality. Symptoms, choice, and location were unconsciously determined through a regressive Identification with a greatly admired and envied boyhood friend. The friend had earlier suffered this kind of physical limitation from poliomyelitis.

(4) In the shadow of "important" people; basking in reflected glory

The following instance illustrates a similar type of Identification in which mannerisms and traits are adopted because of a wish for social success.

Case 41
Friendship and Identification with One who is More Socially Successful

Bob R. had almost never dated girls, and had not been socially prominent during the early days of his high school career; facts which he very much regretted.

However, in his senior year he managed to become very good friends with Sam, one of the social lights among his contemporaries. In a short time it became quite evident that Bob had adopted many of the mannerisms and characteristics of his new friend.

This type of mannerism and trait adoption takes place more prominently in the impressionable and suggestible type of adult, but is by no means confined to them. Many kinds of emotional needs may enhance or lead to its development. Among these is the interesting one which I like to refer to as *basking in reflected glory*. This was a likely factor in the preceding cases. This phenomenon can frequently be observed in the shadow of "important" people. When encountered the "importance" is of course a matter of the subjective evaluation and assessment by the basker. Thus it can be a matter of strictly personal significance; position and prominence; or some combination.

Hereby people seek and may secure a certain measure of prestige through association and through Identification. Basking in reflected glory may be observed in connection with leading political figures, artists, orators, the President, a senator, premier, king or queen, successful professionals in many fields, and indeed any personage regarded as successful or renowned. The adoption of traits, mannerisms, or behavioral features in those who seek such association is not uncommon. Other variations of this phenomenon will be mentioned and illustrated as we proceed.

E. CHARACTEROLOGIC IDENTIFICATION

It is an expected progression that Identification can lead further to characterologic development and change. This brings out a most important function of this mechanism. Thus, it can play a major role in personality development, in the origins of one's interests and ambitions, and in the adoption of major character traits. The following is the summary of an instance of this kind of development.

Case 42
Identification in Personality Development

Helen, a young married woman, had been an only child in a home disrupted by violent disagreements, excessive drinking, and divorce. Her mother, after divorcing the girl's father, soon married a second alcoholically habituated man. From an early juncture, the second husband mostly ignored both Helen and her mother, whether in drunken aloofness, or in a state of depressed sobriety.

Helen's mother was an aggressive kind of pseudo-intellectual woman who associated with individuals comprising the more undisciplined and less successful fringes of the art and theatrical world. Preoccupied with her own frustrations, and often motivated by the ideas of her Bohemian friends, her usual attitudes concerning her daughter resulted in her viewing her as a boring and encumbering obligation.

Rejected by her mother, ignored by her step-father, and confused by the behavior of her mother's acquaintances, Helen found little with which she could identify herself in this shifting and unstable home environment. By the time her mother and step-father finally separated, she was of college age.

In college, Helen hesitantly began an art curriculum, which fortunately she found pleased her mother. Gradually she began to have more and more interest in the abstract art forms which were emphasized by a professor in the Art Department who was greatly admired by her mother.

The professor represented the first stable, well-established person with whom Helen had been able to maintain contact for any length of time. He took a considerable friendly interest in her, and she found herself admiring and being drawn to him. Quite consciously and deliberately she copied his artistic style, but unconsciously and more significantly she also adopted many of his social opinions, verbal expressions, vocal inflections, and physical gesticulations.

Helen longed for her mother's acceptance and recognition, but she also felt extremely hostile toward her for her rejection, and in turn had rejected much about her. Instead of identifying herself with her mother's actual personality and life-role, Helen unconsciously identified herself with an admired person who was quite different from mother, but one whom her

127

mother "happened to" admire and respect. There are a number of interesting elements here, among which it is clear that she still unconsciously sought to gain her mother's acceptance. This helped to determine this particular man as her object of Identification.

Through this young lady's Identification with her professor, her personality development was greatly influenced, the direction of her interests and ambitions was more definitely established, and major character traits were unconsciously adopted. Her's was an instance of a major characterologic kind of Identification.

F. IDENTIFICATION WITH PUBLIC FIGURES; MASS IDENTIFICATION

(1) Prominence inviting identification

As referred to earlier, Identifications may be made with people of prominence in almost any field. These have been on an individual basis. With some of these prominent people who attract a widespread public appeal and interest, however, the process can affect groups of people, or even a segment of the population. The result can be a large-scale reaction which might be regarded as a psychologic kind of epidemic. While not confined to our culture, it is perhaps more prominent as a social phenomenon of the American scene. This phenomenon is one I would call *Mass Identification*. It is greatly facilitated by modern mass communication media; radio, TV, movies, and so forth. Like a tide, it ebbs and flows. History has rarely seen this phenomenon more active than in recent years with the American woman and Jackie Kennedy.

Mass Identification is well illustrated through the influence of prominent successful figures in the entertainment world. For a time they can exert a powerful influence on the tastes, dress, and behavior of a greater or lesser segment of the population. Teen-age groups are particularly responsive to this type of Mass Identification.

(2) Entertainment figures and Mass Identification

Every few years, through entertainment media, the American public adopts certain forceful personalities who for a time come to serve as the archetype for a particular method of expression. There has been a long series of popular singers and movie stars.

A recent instance was that of Elvis Presley, a very successful exponent of "Rock and Roll," who was characterized by his original style, an appeal to many, and a strong projection of himself to his audience.

Part of Elvis Presley's success in the music field was related perhaps to his somewhat unique, though not entirely original, appearance. It was certainly characteristic. His hair was long and swept back to a point, while his sideburns extended half way down to his jaw. His facial expression while singing conveyed to some a study of frozen passion, with his mouth slightly open, and eyelids partly closed. His clothes usually consisted of a "loud" sport shirt, open at the neck, with collar pulled up, trousers which were narrow at the cuff, and dark suede shoes.

His admirers have been mostly teen-agers. There was a fair segment of them at one time who consciously and unconsciously patterned various aspects of their dress, facial expressions, hair cut, or behavior after him. Among this group these traits became an acceptable and admired form of expression, although not always approved by others. As an interesting sidelight, an enterprising hair dresser in a small Michigan town was among those who capitalized on this. He created a hair style *à la* Presley for young girls, and within a few weeks had made a great success, as the tall, the short, the thin, and the stout came trooping in to have their hair done in this fashion.

Prominent figures in many fields have provided the public with an opportunity for similar reactions through the ages. Similar influences on this kind of basis have been exerted to varying degrees on larger or smaller segments of the population.

(3) Contributions to public fashions, styles, and attitudes

Mass Identifications have contributed to numerous fashion changes, fads, styles, and public attitudes. To a lesser extent the long-term development and evolution of the public's philosophy, morals, religion, and legal concepts have been so influenced by prominent figures and leaders.

G. A MAJOR INFLUENCE IN LEARNING

It is hardly possible to overstress the many influences which the operation of Identification can have on learning. Admiration and liking for a teacher can lead in this way to an increased and sometimes lasting interest in his course. Learning can be facilitated tremendously through such constructive kinds of Identifications. As illustrated in *Case 42*, this can progress to the point of influencing or even fully determining one's choice of life work.

Thus, Identification with a liked and admired person can lead to a major commitment in his field of endeavor. This kind of Identification can have an important bearing on one's "choice" of interests. It can have a tremendous effect on one's facility in, and level of, learning, and on one's entire life.

H. "BAD" IDENTIFICATIONS

(1) Socially non-constructive; the "bad" influence for children

Most instances of Identification and learning are constructive, that is, they lead to individual progress in a socially approved fashion. However, this is not always so. It would be a mistake to assume that all Identifications are "good" in this sense.

"Bad" or non-constructive Identifications are also made in many ways. These may be superficial and of little importance. They may be major, lead to personally and/or socially destructive consequences, and can be a symptom of, or contribute in a major way to emotional illness. Identifications are sometimes made with an aggressor, a bad leader, or even a criminal, as we shall see shortly.

"Bad" Identifications also influence learning in a converse way to the preceding discussion. The person sometimes spoken of as a "bad influence" for children or teenagers may be thus because of a propensity of the child or teen-ager to identify with him. Recent state campaigns have been held for parents to "set a good example" in their driving practices for their children.

(2) Parental attitudes and traits automatically adopted, even though unwanted and unrecognized

One should not drive "keeping an eye out for the police," run stop signs, or engage in incautious or unlawful driving habits. Dad should not exceed the speed limit and have Johnnie watch out the rear window for police cars. Some unconscious Identification and taking over of parental attitudes and characteristics takes place inevitably, as well as conscious emulation, and through a combination of the two, father's driving practices, good or bad, can often more readily become son's.

The unconscious adoption of parental traits or behavior through Identification is by no means confined to those which are "good" and approved of by the child. Indeed, *some of the "bad" disapproved ones are also almost inevitably taken over from each parent.* Because of one's personal disapproval of them, these are even more inaccessible to conscious awareness.

I. COMPATHY: AFFECTIVE IDENTIFICATION

(1) Sympathy, empathy and compathy

The degree of emotional sharing, as well as the ability to do this, varies greatly among people. A capacity for such sharing is a distinguishing feature of man. Its depth and genuineness are often a good measure of adulthood and relative maturity.

A number of types of Identification have been discussed. Mention has been made of the conscious placing of oneself in another's shoes. The term and concept of *empathy* has been presented, in which there is a *projective* type of Identification which allows and helps secure an objective awareness and understanding of another's emotional feelings and their meaning, and an adequate appreciation of their extent.

A capacity for empathy is valuable to everyone, and is essential to those in the behavioral sciences, and especially so for the psychotherapist.

Sympathy is also a type of projective Identification, but more superficial. It generally entails feelings of sorrow, pity, or compassion *for* another's grief, loss, hurt, or misfortune.

There is a closer kind of emotional sharing. It is an *affective* type of Identification in which an emotional feeling is literally shared with another. It is not so much a feeling *for,* as a feeling *with*. This close kind of emotional sharing I have termed *compathy*.

Compathy is stronger, deeper, closer, and of a different order than sympathy. It is to be distinguished from empathy, as noted above.

(2) Compathy facilitated through close relationships; individual and group compathy

Compathy is far more likely to occur with persons who share a close interpersonal relationship, although this is not a requisite.

131

While the feelings experienced do not have to be present to an equal extent, they must be the same in kind. However, their level is often fairly close. Compathy is most frequent individually. Instances of Group Compathy are sometimes encountered also.

The following instance is a brief illustration of this interesting, warm, human capacity in which there was the compathic communication and sharing of sadness.

Case 43
Group Compathy; Emotional Feelings of Sadness are Shared

A 48-year-old lawyer died unexpectedly leaving a widow and two children. After the funeral and necessary business arrangements were completed (a period of several months) it was decided that their wisest course of action would be to join relatives on the West Coast. This represented quite an emotional wrench, since they had lived in their home for years and had many long-standing friendships. Although difficult, the discussions about it and the final reaching of the decision were made with at least outward calm.

On the day they drove away, a small group of neighbors gathered to wish them a good trip and farewell. Several were very close friends, and several not. Suddenly, as if in response to a signal, everyone began to weep, in a sudden contagion of sadness. The objective basis of loss varied considerably. This was a striking instance of compathy, as an emotional close sharing of strong feelings with those departing. The level of shared feelings seemed approximately equal.

The above is a rather dramatic example. Compathy operates widely and far less obviously in a great variety of interpersonal situations. Parents, for example, may sometimes literally experience themselves the pleasures and successes, or the difficulties and rebuffs of their children. This kind of close affective Identification may be present for the reader of a novel or the viewer of a play, TV drama, or movie.

A live "real" person nor an actual relationship with him is not an absolute requirement for compathy to exist. One may share closely the actor's feelings. Indeed, some persons have such an acute capacity for this kind of compathic Identification that they can stand to see few movies, or even none at all.

(3) Definition

We can define compathy as *the close sharing of emotional feelings with another person.* Compathy is an *affective kind of*

132

Identification through which one may subjectively experience the emotions of another. It is semi-automatic and independent of voluntary control or direction. Certain distinctions have been noted between this kind of emotional sharing and both empathy and sympathy.

J. IN ADVERTISING: THE SECONDARY APPEAL

(1) The Primary Appeal : toward the direct satisfaction of a need

Advertising men in the last several decades have learned well the value of creating or cultivating what I like to call "Secondary Appeal." Wanting to purchase a drink to satisfy thirst, food to satisfy hunger, or a tool to use for a purpose is the *Primary Appeal* of a given product.

Seeking to stimulate sales by encouraging other interests or needs which are less direct is the *Secondary Appeal*. Many kinds of sales result from this type of advertising. In this endeavor an important aspect relates to promoting Identification or the desire for Identification, usually with admired people or persons of envied status of one kind or another who use, or who are implied users of, the product.

(2) The Secondary Appeal : sought through the encouragement of identification

A prominent popular person is pictured in an advertisement using a given product. If one wants to be like him, using the same product is one way, admittedly small, but still the implication thus conveyed is important to many people and can both wittingly and unwittingly exert considerable influence. The "status symbol" is also an important factor in advertising and in sales, in which the Identification kind of secondary appeal can operate.

An individual with widely admirable attributes or position, and so forth, may be pictured with a product; examples: manliness for men, loveliness for women. The "Marlboro man," the helicopter pilot for Camel, the adventurer-explorer series of Canadian Club are instances. The establishment of sexual allure is the often not-too-subtle Secondary Appeal in perfume advertising: "Just be like our lovely lady (being embraced here), buy this perfume (which of course accounts for her success) and you too can be irresistible and have such a man," the ads seem to say.

133

(3) *Instances illustrating the employment of the Secondary Appeal*

Other important Secondary Appeals sought by this route are by encouraging Identification with: (*a*) wealth (as in the lush surroundings of fine car ads), (*b*) prestige (as in the "Men of Distinction" series, and as exemplified in the rise of the Homburg hat following President Eisenhower's inauguration), (*c*) intelligence and learning (as in the "Great Books" ads and those for various schools, and so forth), and (*d*) snob appeal (witness the slogan: "A title on the door . . . rates a Bigelow on the floor"); and many others. An attentive eye to billboards, magazines, or to other forms of advertising media will disclose these and other instances of Secondary Appeal in profusion and in widely varied applications.

K. IDENTIFICATION IN MILITARY LIFE

(1) *Identification necessary for group morale*

Many forms of Identification are to be encountered in military service. Some of these serve vital personal needs and some have a very important function to the service. Identification with one's outfit is widely recognized as necessary for morale (for instance, the proud statement, "I belong to the best damn outfit in the whole army!"). It promotes security, loyalty, a useful feeling of belonging, a sense of personal value and worth, working together for the mutual good and success of one's unit, mutual confidence, comradeship, and pride.

In the following instance, which has a light overtone, a young airman-to-be began his Identification early. This process was on a fairly superficial level. While largely, and especially at first, a matter of conscious effort, part of it was unwitting and was consciously denied. Its vehemence at times was surprising, and reflected a certain amount of unconscious operation.

Case 44
Military Identification Begins Before the Fact

A 22-year-old college graduate was called into the Air Force through the AFROTC. He had always been of a retiring nature, shying away from most social engagements, while maintaining an excellent academic standing. At the time of activation he had hoped to enter graduate school, a plan which had to be deferred, at least pending completion of his tour with the Air Force.

From almost the receipt of notice, he began to use, in a quite newly acquired aggressive style, the slang and profanity he anticipated to be common to his new associates. Soon after beginning duty, he was outdoing most of them, both in extent and in diversity of occasion, using the new language regardless of who was present, and so on.

The word "we" came to be used constantly in reference to anything done by the Air Force; even the most tremendous world-wide accomplishments were "ours," or accomplished by "us"! It was apparent that he had identified himself rather thoroughly, both with his immediate new surroundings and with the Air Force.

The defensive intent of this operation lies in his gaining strength by identifying with this large, established, and powerful group. Hereby he combats anxiety and insecurity. His identity and role become more certain and established. By "fitting in" as he viewed it, he also conforms to the pattern and is thereby accepted and assimilated.

(2) Individual identifications perpetuating the system

The system of a military organization tends to be perpetuated through the establishment of patterns of behavior. These come to be associated with, and expected from, one in a given position. It is seen very briefly in the following instance. There are similarities here to the phenomenon of Identification with the Aggressor, pages 149–152.

Case 45
Trainee Identifies with Trainer

The Armed Forces sometimes unwittingly utilize the mechanism of Identification in the perpetuation of principles and practices in the training of recruits. Drill instructors are selected and trained for their ability to handle men in a brisk, impersonal, "military" manner. The acceptance of a rather complete level of control of the men, by their instructor, is daily drilled into the recruits for twelve weeks, until it becomes almost literally a part of them.

At the end of the Basic Training period, few of the recruits would be willing to admit that they admired their Drill

Instructor. Often they resent him and his practices. Nonetheless, his attitudes and methods are to an extent (partly consciously and partly unconsciously) taken over, adopted, and absorbed by many of them. The Identification which occurs helps to reenforce tendencies to follow the known and the experienced anyway. As a consequence, when they in turn subsequently come to be put in charge of troops, they well know how the Drill Instructor acted. Things tend usually to be done in very similar fashion to the way he did them. The earlier style and patterns tend to be reproduced. These principles apply in many added ways in military indoctrination and service. They also operate in related fashion in many civilian situations.

(3) Identification wtih a superior and the enhancement of security

In the military service as elsewhere, security is sought (and sometimes found) through Identification with a successful and established leader or superior. This may be a defense operation particularly vital to the novice and tyro.

In the following instance, a brand new naval ensign adopted the particular individual mannerisms and some characteristic items of dress of his commanding officer.

Case 46
Identification in a Newly-Commissioned Naval Officer

Just out of Officer Candidate School during World War II, a young Ensign reported for active duty to his first ship, a small patrol craft. He was originally from the midwest and had had no sea-going experience. He was assigned to the position of Gunnery Officer. The Commanding Officer was an ex-enlisted Gunner's Mate. He liked the young officer and spent a considerable amount of time with him. He helped him to organize his department, to schedule exercises, to train his men, and so on.

It soon became apparent to his fellow officers that the new ensign was identifying with his Commanding Officer. He gradually adopted some of the C.O.'s mannerisms and dress. He took to wearing a baseball cap, constantly carrying a cup of coffee with him, wearing his shirt collar turned up, and even bought himself a pair of high shoe boots.

All of the items adopted were characteristics and habits of the commanding officer. The Identification became appar-

136

ent to many members of the crew. It continued unchanged for some 6–8 months when it began to slowly fade, apparently as a result of increased confidence in himself and in his developing ability to adequately run the gunnery department, without the captain's assistance and close over-the-shoulder supervision.

His Identification was partly conscious and partly unwitting, as he never was able to recognize its full extent. It undoubtedly served an important defensive purpose to him. As the need lessened, in this instance the outward evidences likewise lost their prominence.

L. GROUP IDENTIFICATION

(1) Gregariousness and belonging to organizations

Many people seek Identification with a group. We join churches, lodges, civic groups, social and professional organizations, unions, alumni groups, classes, patriotic groups, political bodies, and many others. There are at least several contributing factors usually present, including man's gregariousness, perhaps on a deeper level the herd instinct, more superficial social reasons, finding friends or possible mates, promoting a worthy cause, and so forth.

Affiliation with a group, however, can also be an important security operation and one which is often pursued unwittingly. Indeed, all kinds of plausible explanations and Rationalizations may be advanced to obscure the defensive aspects of one's group Identifications. He also gains allies, supporters, and friends. He is less alone. When this mechanism is operative in this fashion we might refer to it as *Group Identification.*

(2) Group Identification and the seeking of acceptance, security, support, strength, and belonging

"In union there is strength" is a principle which applies to the individual and to his joining an organization, as well as to states and to the nation. Thus, Identification with a group can offer a person in varying degree a feeling of strength, perhaps a sense of common endeavor, brotherhood, acceptance, and belonging. One identifies thus with something bigger and stronger, some of which strength then accrues to him.

137

Group Identifications can serve an important individual need. They can also serve very useful social purposes. Partly because of the defensive value of such Identification, people participate in many highly constructive and commendable activities. Certain individuals who are less secure and whose maturity is less developed, often thereby make all kinds of highly useful social contributions which might not otherwise be made.

M. VICARIOUS SATISFACTIONS

(1) The seeking of gratifications not otherwise available

To some extent everyone secures satisfactions vicariously. These can vary from a superficial Identification with, and experiencing, to a point where one becomes almost lost in a vicarious role. In the most extreme cases of the latter, a parent, for example, can come to live *through* a child. Much of our foregoing discussion bears on this subject. Such satisfactions and the unconscious seeking of them are an important part of the Endogain (the unconscious primary gain); the very basis, or *raison d'être* of the major mental mechanism of Identification.

The needs and gratifications which are sought in vicarious fashion may be personally forbidden and disapproved. As a consequence, they may only be possible in these guises. It is hardly surprising that conscious awareness of this very interesting kind of substitutive experiencing and living may be limited. Vicarious phenomena can subserve vital intrapsychic needs, constituting an important internal defensive operation.

The following instance, reported earlier [14] illustrates an interesting type of important substitutive gratification which can be sought vicariously through the operation of Identification. This type of endeavor can be completely unconscious. It is frequently at least partly so. As in this case, it can have a major influence on one's interests and activities, and in one's entire life.

Case 47
Vicarious Satisfaction Through Identification

A fifty-two-year-old bachelor had developed an increasing interest in the theater as the years progressed. Certain attempts in the direction of courtship and marriage had been unsuccessful and he had never found a wife. Although he professed great satisfaction with the advantages and freedom of remaining single, there were strong secret desires for married life and a family. His interest in the theater was partially rationalized on a conscious level as being simply on the basis of his interest in the art *per se*.

The plays which he never missed and which he, in fact, would see repeatedly, were ones in which a happy married life was portrayed. By identifying himself with the head of the family in the theatrical production, he secured considerable vicarious satisfaction.

Later he joined an amateur theatrical group in which he was never happier than when allowed to play the occasional bit part of a family head. He had very little conscious awareness of what motivated him, and much of the underlying need for the gratification which he secured was unconscious.

(2) A vicarious life

The Vicarious Satisfactions which may be sought or secured play an interesting and important role in the operation of Identification. These may be minor and conscious. They may run the gamut to being of such a major extent as to the situation in which a person attempts to live his life through another. A father who always wanted to be a lawyer or physician may unwittingly pressure his son into it. An author may live vicariously through a character; a lawyer through his clients; a teacher through his students; a parent through a child; or a physician through his patients. One may come thus to lead a vicarious life.

These kinds of satisfactions must not become too prominent for the professional man. The dangers to maintaining a clear objectivity are obvious. This is particularly true for the psychiatrist. Sufficient satisfactions must be available from other sources; other interpersonal relationships, family, and other areas of living, and so on, so as to relegate any such vicarious living to a minor role indeed.

N. THE "PERSONAL YARDSTICK" IN NEW RELATIONSHIPS: THE IDENTIFICATION OF A NEW ACQUAINTANCE WITH SOMEONE FROM EARLIER EXPERIENCE

(1) The conditioning effect of earlier relationships

This is a concept of major importance in the science of interpersonal relations. Early relationships have an important conditioning effect for subsequent ones. There is a strong tendency to evaluate and to "see" a new person, in the light of the relationship with an earlier (and usually important) person from the past.

Generally, some similarities are present which stimulate a subjective Identification. Often enough these are even relatively gross ones, such as age, size, build, or coloring. They also may be quite minor or subtle in helping to trigger such a reaction. The "repeated relationship" which may be anticipated and experienced to various degrees is often enough a distorted one. One can be led unwittingly into all kinds of false expectations, judgments, and evaluations.

(2) Applying the "personal yardstick" to new acquaintances

However, the use of one's past experiences as a kind of measuring device for future ones is most understandable. This is the important concept of the *Personal Yardstick,* presented earlier.[19] Although subject to all kinds of inaccuracies, which are not readily accessible to awareness, it is a necessary and vital measuring device. We all use it. It is, at least early in life, the only one available. We are accordingly hardly surprised to find it operating rather automatically in the realm of one's interpersonal relations.

My then 15-year-old daughter returned from a visit with friends in Atlanta. "Why," she exclaimed, "June is *just like* [younger sister] Barbara!" And later, in discussing another of our friend's children, she said, "You know, Jim was *exactly like* [younger brother] Bob!" How alike were they really? Certainly they were from the general standpoint of approximate age, and what this means in terms of capacity, performance, and behavior. There were some superficial character trait resemblances, but there the similarities ended. Each had their assets and handicaps, but they were actually quite individual and different in most areas of temperament, personality, and interests. Still, on the basis of being closest to other people of established relationship, they were visualized—and reacted to—as being "just like." This was her familiar frame of reference.

(3) Widespread instances of the application of the "personal yardstick"

Dr. James R. commented, "You know, I liked him instantly. He reminded me of a swell colleague from service days." An attractive young woman patient explained, "I felt strongly attracted to him from the first. He resembles Hal [an old childhood sweetheart] so very much!" Another patient said, "I knew that guy [a local businessman] was a stinker from the word 'go.' I knew I would have trouble with him. He is just like old 'Study Hall' Saul." [A high school principal with whom this man had had many difficulties.]

A lawyer reported, "As soon as we met the Judge, I was uneasy about going to trial. I know why. He reminded me right off of old Judge B." [A tough and rigid jurist encountered in the lawyer's early days of practice.]

(4) A stimulus for the initial response to a new acquaintance

These kinds of Identifications are by no means always so well present in conscious awareness. They can exist completely outside of awareness, to account for all kinds of "unaccountable" emotional responses toward other people. They can help to determine initial reactions, love and affection, prejudices, (degree of) acceptance or rejection, and so on, toward and for another person.

A male patient talked interminably of his harsh, distant and unapproachable boss. Eventually, after much hard work, he came to recognize (and to appreciate the important consequences to him in living); that (a) he had made an unconscious Identification of his boss with his father, and (b) he had in error "assigned" to the boss, or magnified certain ones of his (existing) traits, which in actuality were those of his father.

(5) Why is the personal yardstick applied? What are the advantages?

Operation of the Personal Yardstick in conjunction with Identifications with people (especially significant ones) from the past can be thought of in several ways. These include: (a) a matter of psychologic convenience and familiarity, (b) the utilization of existing experience, (c) the conditioning effect of the earlier relationship, (d) an instance of a type of "repetition compulsion," and (e) following "habits" or patterns in one's interpersonal relations.

Thus, earlier relationships set up a representation which is more easily matched in later experiences; a shadow which lingers and which is more readily filled; more easily given substance anew, at a later date.

In summary, the Identification of a new acquaintance with a person from one's earlier experience is a frequent phenomenon in interpersonal relationships. This is an example of some other important types of Identification which do not clearly fit into our earlier definition. Through this type, a person may be "perceived" almost as though he were another person known earlier. This may be stimulated or reenforced at times through (major or minor) items of physical or of characterologic similarity. As a consequence of this important type of Identification, the new person may be seen, judged, and dealt with as was the earlier one. Similar views, attitudes, judgments, reactions, and behavior may come to be anticipated. The wide room for inaccuracy, distortion, and subsequent disappointment or hurt is apparent.

(6) The fostering of recapitulation, with the potential for major and minor inaccuracies and distortions

The degree of use of this type of Identification has considerable individual variation. However, *this tendency to set up inaccurate representations of new relationships, on the basis of prior experience with earlier figures is much more widely prevalent than is commonly recognized.* It accounts for many, many problems in interpersonal relationships. The later relationships tend to recapitulate the earlier one in the subjective experience and expectations of the person who has unconsciously made the Identification.

The clarification of this use of the mechanism of Identification together with its very important implications and consequences is an important part of the therapeutic learning process in every analysis.

3. IDENTIFICATION WITH SIGNIFICANT ADULTS

A. PARENTAL IDENTIFICATIONS BY THE CHILD

The most important role of Identification is in early childhood. The influence upon children through Identification with adults who are significant to them cannot be overestimated. The function of this mechanism in their personality and character trait development is a most major one.

In the earlier days, there is what might be regarded as an "overlapping" of identities. The differentiation between self and mother is unclear. In effect there exists an almost complete Identification of the infant with its mother. As the child grows, the ego becomes more clearly differentiated. Orgel [19] regards Identification as the original form of an emotional tie with a love object. O'Kelly and Muckler [18] explain that it is by Identification with their parents that children become socialized.

In such early Identifications with a parent or a parental figure, the child accepts aspects of the person either as they actually are, or as they may be perceived by him. Of course, he may come to possibly overvalue them through the added process of Idealization. Quite unconsciously he takes over some of them for himself. In this manner, for example, he may later come to acquire their tastes in food * and clothes. Similarly, the child may come to gradually adopt or take over certain ones of their standards, their viewpoints, and/or their prejudices, as well as aspects of their traits, mannerisms, and behavior. Furthermore, and as a consequence to much of this over a number of important developmental years, Identification is the most important single mechanism in the development of the conscience, or superego.

B. "LIKE FATHER, LIKE SON!" "LIKE MOTHER, LIKE DAUGHTER!"

We know particularly through our understanding of other mechanisms that this kind of adage does not always hold. They are by no means invariable. For many reasons, there are variations, exceptions, and even reversals. However, through the operation of Idealizations and Identifications, example, precept, teaching, and so on, they do have, to varying degrees some nearly universal applications.

An individual may deny, or even vehemently and stubbornly insist, that no traces of parental influence are in evidence in his make-up. Resulting Identifications may be deeply buried and quite outside of conscious awareness, but they are to some extent inevitably present. Such hidden rests are uncovered in the intensive psychotherapy and analysis of every patient. The old proverbs

---

* In this connection, Hella Freud Bernays, who helped with the research for this study, noted that, ". . . my little granddaughter, aged 5, carefully cuts away all traces of fat from the meat on her plate; exactly as she has been seeing her mother (my daughter-in-law) do, during her whole life.

"This stimulated my interest and upon further inquiry I learned that the maternal grandfather also always cut off all fat from his meat. My daughter-in-law, probably unconsciously, has been identifying with her parent in this way, as likely her child is now with her!"

quite often prove to convey accurately a great deal of meaning in understanding human emotion and behavior. Perhaps were this not so, they would not have become proverbs!

C. IMITATION AND IDENTIFICATION

Imitation may be a precedent or a precurser of later Identifications. Conscious imitation may also sometimes accompany them. The following instance was reported by a student.

Case 48
Imitation and Identification

"During the early childhood years of my brother, who is the older son in our family, it was almost constantly obvious to my parents, and less so to me, that he was a persistent and detailed imitator of his father, often to such an extent upon occasion as to evoke Dad's embarrassment. His efforts at imitation were particularly present, for example, in the realm of automobile driving, although there were other facets of Dad's behavior and daily activities which were pretty much repeated in somewhat regular fashion after careful observation by his elder son.

"From the time when he could even stand with reasonable safety, my brother would watch every movement Dad made in the operation of our family automobile. (This was in the day of the floor type of gear shift.) Typically, he would stand just behind the front seat and watch over Dad's shoulder the manipulation of the gear shift, foot pedals and steering wheel. Of course, he also overheard Dad's comments about driving and drivers.

"These observations did not go without making an impression, nor unpracticed. In addition to imitating Dad while driving, his favorite game for a long time was 'driving' his wagon. On one such occasion (observed by my mother, the source of this bit of the story) he was driving his wagon along a gravel driveway and a wheel became stuck. After several futile attempts to disengage the wheel, he took the handle of his wagon, slammed it to the ground, and with a child's expressive indignation exclaimed, 'Damn those brakes!' This was an expression—and behavior—quite typical of father.

"As a postscript to this story, I might add that my brother's interests were not dampened by the punishment he received for swearing. The chief topic of conversation at the dinner table at home still is often about automobiles, their virtues and faults. My brother has long since given up any conscious imitation of Dad behavior-wise, although he very definitely tries to emulate him in business practices and judgments, etc. However, beginning back in the early stages of childhood imitation, he would occasionally (according to mother) quite unconsciously exhibit many small mannerisms of Dad. Today there are a great many aspects of personality and character traits firmly ingrained, so that now the two men bear a striking resemblance to each other personality-wise, as well as physically."

Conscious imitation can, as earlier noted, represent a kind of mockery, an attempt to make something appear ludicrous, or an exaggeration of something not admired or respected. Mostly, however, it is an indication of acceptance, approval, admiration, or respect. It can constitute flattery of the most sincere kind. Imitation often bears the same relation to Identification as justification does to Rationalization; as fear does to anxiety; or as grief does to emotional Depression.

In summary, both imitation and Identification may be a way of indicating approval, acceptance, and love. Conversely, they may constitute an important endeavor to *secure* them. Thus, the earliest form of love relation in human life occurs. The child says, in effect, "Mommy (or Daddy), I love you. I want to be just the way you are."; and/or "I want your love, and shall seek to secure it by being like you."

D. EMOTIONAL CONTAGION; THE COMPATHIC COMMUNICATION OF ATTITUDES AND EMOTIONAL FEELINGS

The taking over of another's emotion or attitude can occur quite readily, automatically, and upon occasion almost instantaneously. This can occur with individuals or groups. Sometimes in the latter this is comparable to an epidemic. Sometimes it is far faster, as in the development, mobilization, and the rapid spread of emotional feelings in a mob.

In the individual contagion of emotion one can sometimes observe interesting examples. We saw the compathic contagion of sadness illustrated in *Case 43* between (principally) adults. Emotional contagion takes place with great facility between adult and child. A small child is quick to be aware of fear, as for example, in his parent. He becomes frightened in turn. There is a compathic communication of anxiety from parent to child in similar fashion. This type of Identification of sharing emotional feelings *with*

145

another occurs widely and in great variety in interpersonal relationships generally and in parent-child relationships in particular.

One may sometimes witness this kind of contagion of emotions or attitudes from adult to child. It took place in the following instance.

Case 49
Emotional Contagion [14]

A 10-year-old boy was given a football by his favorite uncle. Upon his parents' suggestion, he emphasized his thanks with a kiss. The uncle was obviously embarrassed. He thought the boy was too old for kissing, and should have outgrown such a social convention. He did not approve.

Up to this time, the boy himself had had no doubts. He really hadn't given it much thought. However, as he instantly grasped his uncle's embarrassment, he became overwhelmed with embarrassment himself. Such feelings continued henceforth when the possibility of kissing adults arose. His attitude mirrored his uncle's. Now such kissing was to him outmoded and childish. This small incident exerted a powerful conditioning effect. It illustrates the compathic communication of emotional feelings and attitudes from adult to child. It is an emotional kind of contagion.

E. IDENTIFICATION AND PERSONALITY DEVELOPMENT

(1) Major influence on the Superego

In the development of the Superego, or conscience, it has been pointed out that the single most important influence occurs through the process of Identification. It is probably also the most constructive and healthful one in the ordinary course of events. According to Fenichel,[7] Identifications also play a great part in the process of building up the ego of the developing infant. Many authorities recognize this. We have seen how the infant or young child senses changes of mood, apprehension, or anxiety in the parent or other significant adult and makes them his own by the unconscious process of Identification.[14] Such anxiety may be thought of as being communicated to the children from parents; by intuition, by emotional contagion, by compathic communication, or through Identification.

Lorand also attaches considerable importance to the role of Identification in character formation. He declares[16] that during the anal period of personality development, the necessity to obey and to follow instructions in learning to be clean carries with it the necessity of loving the parents (or surrogates) and of obeying their commands. This is seen by him to form the nucleus of the (unconscious) process of Identification which, in turn, ultimately provides the basis for the later formation of the superego. There are two ways in which obedience to parents can be achieved: one way is to love the parent. When this prevails, the child will follow the educational methods employed by the parents and carry out their commands because he loves them. The child identifies with the parents by doing what the parent wants. He wants to please them. The other, much less healthy method, is the result of force and necessity, where the child is afraid of the strong parent, who is able to administer punishment if his instructions are not carried out. The child behaves through his fear, not his love—and the result is the mobilization (and very likely the repression) of resentment, hostility, and hate. My own view would trace vital first Identifications also back earlier, to the oral phase of personality development. These may establish an important precedent for what follows in later stages of maturation.

(2) The significance of early childhood identifications

That the identifications made in early childhood are of great significance for later development of the individual is also confirmed by Lorand [16] who feels that most often character difficulties are a direct consequence of an inability to solve the conflict of the love-and-hate experienced by the small child in his relationships with his parents during the Oedipal period. There must be a healthy solution of the Oedipus complex to bring about the Identification processes essential for normal development. Processes of Identification are likely to loom quite large during the Oedipal period. Too strong an attachment to the parent of the opposite sex may prove to be an obstacle that prevents the resolution of the conflicts present during this period. One unfortunate consequence may be an overstrong Identification with the corresponding parent, rather than the giving up of the parental love-object in the course of maturation, which can then produce faulty character development.

Parents must of course also adjust themselves at times to the child's demands. To allow this, the adults must understand themselves thoroughly enough so that they may have the ability to identify with their growing child and to sense and feel and be sympathetic with his difficulties.

Being a parent is the most complex task in the world. The "good" parent requires the ability to love, to enjoy his child, a measure of detached objectivity, plus an adequate measure of understanding, sympathy, empathy, and compathy.

On Identification Allport [2] writes that there is the development of such close ties with another that one comes to act, at least to an extent, as if he *was* the other. Consciously or unconsciously, various single or multiple traits and characteristics of the other's attitudes or aspects of his personality are reproduced. Parents come to identify with children, and, very important to their future adult personality, children come to identify with their parents. We have observed how one may even come to practically live one's life through the other person; a vicarious kind of living.

F. IDENTIFICATION ENCOURAGED BY PARENTS

I have already discussed briefly the important position which is often occupied by Identification in learning. This is certainly not confined to formal education by any means. One finds it likely to operate in many kinds of learning experience.

Parents sometimes consciously promote efforts to identify on the part of their children. A worthy person or a successful one, and so forth, is held out as an example which they are encouraged to emulate.

Sometimes such an attempt is made deliberately by an adult to encourage self-discipline or to influence behavior, as in the following interesting and rather touching little incident. Herein one again sees a stimulation of an effort to please, the desire for approval. In this instance, the desire to please was directed primarily towards the physician as a parent-surrogate, but also of course, to the father as well.

Case 50
A Standard is Held Up

It was during World War II. An eleven-year-old boy injured his wrist while swinging out and jumping from a rope high on the bank of a stream where he liked to swim. X-rays revealed a dislocation of the navicular bone.

His family physician said to the boy, who was already in tears with pain: "Clench your teeth like a good soldier. This

148

will only hurt for a minute or so." The young boy gritted his teeth, stopped crying, and did not make a sound while the physician manipulated his wrist to reduce the dislocation.

As he was leaving the office, his arm now in a cast, the doctor overheard him ask his father, "Was I a good soldier, Daddy?"

4. IDENTIFICATION WITH THE AGGRESSOR

A. A DEFENSIVE OPERATION

Anna Freud [9] first named another important defensive use of Identification, that of Identification with the Aggressor. She refers to Identification as a factor in the development of the superego, and asserts that by the further use of this process the superego gradually succeeds in making the parents' example its own. In addition, the child can also identify itself *with* aggression that threatens it from the outside, or which is actually being practiced against it. She cites the instance of a child who had suffered much in the way of fear from a teacher who made threatening grimaces. By himself making faces in turn at other children, he was identifying with the dreaded external object, the teacher. It is also important to observe that this type of Identification also stems from various threatening or aggressive aspects of parents and parent-surrogates.

Identification with the threatening person or aggressor is accomplished by the child's introjection of some characteristics of the anxiety-provoking object. Introjection plays an important adjunctive role in this kind of ego-defensive operation.

Alexander [1] also refers to this interesting employment of the mechanism of Identification. He agrees that in this type of its utilization one identifies with the threatening opponent, as a means of allaying anxiety. Through this complex endeavor one may come to impersonate the aggressor. In this way the child transforms himself from the person who is threatened, to become himself the threatening figure.

The child thus may introject the adults' aggression, and direct his own aggressive acts (fantasied or real) against them or others. Identification with the aggressor, within proper limits, is a defensive operation which can be regarded as a part of normal development. By assumption of one's opponent's qualities through the intrapsychic process of Introjection, anxiety is mastered.[14] The enemy is absorbed; one becomes like him and the threat is lessened.

B. IN CHILDREN'S GAMES

This type of development frequently can be seen to enter into children's games. After all, the threatening person becomes much less so if you can become like him, even in make-believe. It can also be a way of "acting out," of devaluing through repetition, and of simply mastering the threatening situation through a reenactment.

It would not be difficult in Case 50 to visualize our young lad playing doctor in this fashion (or playing soldier for somewhat different reasons). A little girl may want to play the nurse after receiving an injection from her (which hurt and frightened). A little boy may want to play dentist after visiting one. After a frightening animal experience (realistic or in fantasy), the child may want to play games in which he takes the part of that animal. After a dream, he may want to act the part of a threatening figure.

In children's games, the close observer can find interesting instances in which there is some Identification with an aggressor. Such roles are often unconsciously determined. The child could not explain its purpose or intent. Taking a part in games in this way is defensively intended to prevent or to neutralize anxiety.

C. IDENTIFICATION, INTERNALIZATION, AND PROJECTION

In rather complex development, these three mechanisms often operate in similar ways, so that at times one can not draw sharp lines of distinction between them, or one mechanism is found defined in terms of another. In the development of the conscience, what the child does is to Internalize other people's criticism of his own behavior. Thus, in one analysis [1] the child criticised the analyst for the very fault of which she herself, the child, was guilty. With criticism thus internalized, the child succeeded in externalizing the offense. In essence this becomes Projection.

One can accordingly see how Identification with the aggressor may be supplemented by another defense mechanism, in which guilt, for example, becomes projected. Fenichel [7] holding to the view that Identification is the very first of all object relations, points out that a later Regression toward its renewed operation may be used in fighting off object relations of all kinds, including fear.

D. IDENTIFICATION WITH ANTICIPATED CENSURE

Kris [12] reported this interesting piece of a child's analysis:

"A little girl was occasionally bossy and negativistic during the session. In the course of the treatment, it was observed that she behaved this way on days when she feared being found out and scolded by her mother for breaking something of the mother's. The mechanism which the child used, Anna Freud's 'identification with the aggressor' was easily brought to her attention, and after repetitions of this behavior occurred, the child came to understand the connection between her destructive acts, her fears and her bossiness. Then, on later occasions, when she was bossy, the analyst could ask: 'What of mother's things have you spoiled today?' "

E. IDENTIFICATION AND INVERSION; A REENFORCEMENT OF REPRESSION

Anna Freud cited a possible example of Identification with an aggressor being found in children's love of animals, which she holds may represent the outcome of an old animal phobia. By identifying with the "aggressive" animal, the child now comes to love it and unconsciously feels as if he himself participates in the animal's strength.

Eventually, the animal which once threatened him becomes a friend. Playing and acting like him may even come to be adopted, replacing a threat to oneself into threatening others. The old fear is further hidden. The original defensive Repression is reenforced by Identification, and the Inversion of the emotional reaction takes place, with fear turning into fondness.

F. PRISONERS OF WAR

Under certain kinds of pressure, adults revert to this rather primitive use of the mechanism of identifying with the aggressor. Many vivid descriptions have come to us from those who have experienced being held in prisoner-of-war or concentration camps. It has been noted, for example, that certain internees come to act toward their fellow-prisoners with the same kind of brutality that they had themselves had to endure from their captors. They came to identify with the enemy.

This type of reaction reflects an Identification with the oppressor; with those in power. A number of interesting variations of this theme have come to light during and since World War II and the Korean War.

151

5. IDENTIFICATION IN EMOTIONAL ILLNESS

A. IN DEPERSONALIZATION; MISIDENTIFICATIONS

In early childhood, unconsciously, incomplete Identifications may take place, or partial ones, or mixed or overlapping ones; all of which can be most confusing to the ego. In the development of the personality, generally a great number of partial and minor identifications are made. Of these, the most important are likely to be the early ones that the child makes with the significant adults in his environment. In the process of personality development, the individual attempts to take on certain aspects of those with whom he comes in contact, especially those which seem admirable or worthy of approval. Such Identifications, as has been noted, may be conscious or unconscious. In normal development, various elements thus become assimilated and integrated in the healthy and mature personality. However, as noted above, if this is not done successfully, and there is only partial Identification, or if there are Identifications in conflict with one another, Depersonalization may result. The development of other Dissociative Reactions may be enhanced.

Identification can play an important role in the production of feelings of Depersonalization and in Fugue States. In Depersonalization there may be confusions in Identification. Misidentifications may be made, through which one's role becomes uncertain or in conflict. These kinds of conflicting Identifications can result in the failure to achieve an adequate personality synthesis. Dissociative phenomena may result, or the basis for this type of psychopathology laid down in the event of later sufficient stress. Misidentification is defined as *the adoption of conflicting aspects or traits of one or more persons, which leads to an uncertainty as to one's role or identity.* Personality inconsistencies and confusion can result, and faulty personality synthesis or subsequent dissociation may follow. Such untoward consequences are facilitated by later psychic stress.

B. IN HYPOCHONDRIA; OVERCONCERN WITH HEALTH, OR HYGEIAPHRONTIS

Identification, as well as parental attitudes through their conditioning effect, can lay the foundation for the development, later in life, of particular types of neurotic reaction. For example, when parents are themselves unduly concerned with matters of health, or are preoccupied with their bodies and bodily reactions, their chil-

152

dren are rather apt to emulate their parents in this regard. The children are likely to develop similar attitudes of overconcern in these areas. This can lay the foundation for the Hygeiaphrontic Reaction (Hypochondriasis).

Klein [11] mentions a case in which ". . . there was no doubt that her [the mother's] attitude had contributed to his [the son's] hypochondriacal fears." In this, Indentification and Introjection play important roles. Kanner [10] regards the "imitation" of adult patterns which the child has had occasion to observe and to become thoroughly familiar with, as a significant source of hypochondriacal attitudes in children. He cites examples of the relation between overconcern with health on the parents' part and the development of the same concerns on the part of children. I have discussed these important relationships elsewhere in the consideration of this particular neurotic reaction.[14]

Upon occasion, Identification can also play a prominent role in the "choice" of symptoms of hypochondriasis. This applies to patients with all types of neurotic reactions. It also can apply to many more transient hypochondriacal concerns, such as the frequent and troubling, but interesting ones, developed by medical students and young physicians through their early contacts with many varieties of pathology and with patients suffering from a wide variety of illnesses. This mechanism can also sometimes be important during the onset of a more acute episode of overconcern with health. Certain of these relationships between Hypochondriasis and Identification are illustrated in the following case, in which the neurotic reaction followed a hygeiaphrontic (hypochondriacal) pattern.

Case 51
Identification in Hypochondriasis (Hygeiaphrontis)

A 32-year-old housewife began to have increasingly severe conflicts over her role as a wife and mother. Her illness took the form of a neurosis, in which the most prominent feature was the rather rapid onset of increasingly troubling and preoccupying hypochondriacal concerns. In studying the onset of her symptoms, the part in this unfortunate sequence of events played by the mechanism of Identification was soon evident.

Dorothy M. had begun to read the obituary columns, with an increasing interest and concern about the deaths of persons her own age and younger. The causes of death were important to her, and partly through Identification, she began to look for, to worry about, and then finally to experience various symptoms which she believed to characterize certain of these illnesses.

153

The process of Identification in this fashion extended to include her friends who became ill. Soon she worried almost constantly over illness, symptoms, and bodily function. In this fashion, she "found" important sources of worry and concern which, among other purposes, served as a diversionary focus of attention and interest away from her more basic emotional conflicts. On a number of occasions, through a process of Identification, she developed subjective symptoms like those of friends or family members.

C. CONVERSION REACTIONS (HYSTERIA)[14]

The Hysterical Personality is marked by an unusual capacity for imitativeness and for Identification with others. This is often reflected in symptom formation in the Conversion Reactions. Such Identification is usually outside of and beyond conscious awareness. By this mental mechanism, the person unconsciously takes over the characteristics of another's personality or molds himself after another. It accordingly becomes "easier" for some patients, especially of the hysterical group, to develop the same symptoms that have been seen in others; sometimes this even includes those that have not been seen, but merely heard about!

As an example of how this mechanism can operate, a middle-aged woman developed a painful tight throat on a psychological basis during the course of psychotherapy. At the height of its progression she couldn't speak above a whisper and the discomfort was rather severe. A close companion had developed throat cancer which was progressive and inexorable in its course. While it would be an oversimplification to ascribe the development of these symptoms to Identification, nevertheless the operation of this mechanism played a significant role. The symptoms expressed, among other meanings, her suffering for and with her good friend. Further, life in general was threatening, constrictive, and appeared to be closing in on her.

This kind of Identification helps provide a foundation for the development of various hysterical symptoms. With regard to the Conversion Reactions, it has been found, for instance, that children with hysterical parents are much more likely to develop the same kinds of personality traits and Conversion manifestations as their parents, through the complex workings of the mechanisms of Idealization, Identification, and Incorporation. In Conversion Hysteria, we are apt to find: Conversion, Repression, Distortion, and Symbolism. There may also be Condensation, Displacement, Extension, or Elaboration. There may also be multiple Identifications.

In the development of the hysterical group of character defenses, Identification always plays a part. There may be hostile Identification, confined largely to hostile and rejecting elements of the personality of the parent. It is a tragic fact that a non-rational process such as this usually tends to assure the loss of the very goal that is unconsciously sought. With the Hysterical Personality, as with others, it is as if he said in effect: "If I become like you, perhaps I will get the love, the acceptance and the affection that I so much want."

D. IN OTHER NEUROTIC AND PSYCHOTIC REACTIONS

Space does not permit mention of all the ways in which Identification enters into emotional illness. There are many and we can mention only a few. Young [25] sees excessive Identification in the self-pity of the neurotic patient who takes on the burdens of his fellows, or even of the whole world. This may lead only to sentimentality and romanticism, but if it goes on to an exaggerated degree, it can result in a loss of contact with reality.

In some psychotic reactions, Regression leads to a vagueness of personal identity. According to Klein,[11] failure to maintain Identification with both internalized and real loved objects may result in psychotic disorders, such as depressive states, mania, or paranoia.

In serious emotional illness Identification can have psychopathologic sequelae which are very serious. This is seen in its ultimate form in the psychoses. Misidentifications occur in many forms in the psychotic reactions. *External* ones refer to those involving other patients, visitors, staff personnel, and so on; those which involve individuals external to the patient. Some of these are delusional and most serious.

Other misidentifications are *internal* and involve the self. These are the type more related to our present discussion. Thus, there are patients in every large mental hospital for example, who have identified themselves, in a psychotic use of this mechanism, with famous people. The following case is illustrative.

Case 52
Identification in Psychotic Reactions [14]

A psychotic patient developed a delusional system in which he believed himself to be Christ. The process of Identification

155

was so complete and so beyond reality that the patient sought to live and act the part. This he did in many ways and most of the time.

As in the foregoing case, there are likely to be found "Napoleons," "Julius Caesars," and "Jesus Christs" among the psychotic patients of many large mental hospitals. The completeness of these instances of internal and personal identification vary greatly. At times there are evident (to others) glaring inconsistencies and incongruities of which the patient is seemingly unaware.

6. THERAPY

Identification may be made by the patient with the psychotherapist, especially in situations of positive transference. This is a not uncommon development, the possibility of which the therapist must be constantly aware, and it can require quite delicate management. According to Bergler,[3] what is important in analysis is to find out, not whom the patient identifies with, but the reason for the specific partial Identification.

Sometimes Identifications with the therapist are interesting and at times quite important. One psychiatrist friend who wears a mustache has observed that many of his male patients experiment with mustaches themselves after several weeks in psychotherapy. Another, who smokes a pipe regularly, has noticed that several of his male patients have switched to pipes from cigarettes after a period of treatment.

The alert therapist, of course, hopes to become aware of all kinds of existing and long-standing Identifications during the course of the therapeutic work, as well as any which may develop during a given period of treatment. Their analysis and the resulting understanding which is secured can be of great personal value to the patient. Needless to say, all of this is often far from easy to achieve. There are all kinds of resistances to securing the necessary increase in self-awareness. These do not give way readily.

7. DYNAMICS

A. MOTIVES

(1) The seeking of acceptance, belonging, and love

Through Identifications, we have seen how certain satisfactions and gratifications can be achieved. These may be vicarious ones,

156

perhaps otherwise forbidden, and possible only in these unconscious guises. The major underlying motive for Identification is the desire for love, for acceptance, or approval. The resulting Identification may vary from something rather simple and superficial to something complex and deeply unconscious.

The poet William Blake (1757–1827), with sensitive and intuitive understanding, stated the basis, or *raison d'être* and goal, of Identification when he wrote: "And then I'll . . . be like him, and he will then love me." As we know, however, Identification may also subserve other unconscious needs, for example because of guilt feelings or in ensuing punishment, or other internal needs of a less kindly nature.

(2) Prestige and ego building

Identification may serve a prestige function. This it does when the individual says, in effect, "I think you are fine (or great, or loved, or famous, or gifted, or clever, or distinguished) and so I am going to be the way you are." We have learned that Identification may be made with parents, with movie or stage heroes, with one's employer or social superior, with a lover, with a military or popular hero, with the President, with royalty, with an aggressor, with a criminal or wrongdoer, with a sports champion, and so on.

Out of all conscious awareness, a person's accent, hairdress, mannerisms, gait, and so forth may reflect the process of Identification. O'Kelly and Muckler [18] regard it as adaptive when it strengthens effectiveness in manipulating reality. They see in it the assimilation of those characteristics of others that contribute to satisfaction of need and to the reduction of anxiety.

(3) The seeking to be like an admired or envied person

The following instance illustrates what perhaps used to be a more common phenomenon; taking over the qualities of an admired movie star. Today's TV personalities can stimulate similar reactions.

Case 53
Identification with a Movie Star

A housewife became intensely interested in a certain glamorous movie star. A considerable portion of her time and energy was spent in gathering all kinds of information about the star's life. It became gradually apparent to her friends (but not to her!) that certain movements, gestures, and responses of the star had been "taken over" by their friend. She had identified with the actress to such an extent that she had unwittingly adopted certain attributes, which she associated with the idealized star.

Approval, acceptance, and love are common goals sought through the operation of this dynamism. Identification differs from Projection (by which intolerable qualities are disowned by imputing them to another) in that as a consequence elements of another's personality are reproduced within oneself. The motivation originates, as indicated earlier, in the wish to be like the other person. The sought-after result will be greater approval from the self, and increased acceptance or love from the object. Others will approve, respect, or love more also. (Must they not also like and admire the person and his attributes even, as does the identifier?) Self-approval may come to supplement, to equate, or to replace approval from others. Other motives also have been noted.

One might in this light consider, for example, some of the rationale behind some of the old proverbs such as "When in Rome, do as the Romans do."

B. IDENTIFICATION WITH A CRIMINAL

Frequently when there has been a particularly newsworthy and violent crime, a number of people will come forward to "confess" a crime they could not possibly have committed. Repressed violent impulses and other unconscious factors account for the Identification with the criminal. This was illustrated in a famous West Coast murder case some years ago.

Case 54
Multiple Confessions for a Murder [14]

At the time of the notorious "Black Dahlia" murder case on the West Coast some years ago, a number of persons came forward and "confessed" the crime. Investigation proved them to be innocent. They had *identified* themselves so thoroughly with the actual murder that several of them actually believed that they had committed the crime. The lurid facts of the murder sufficiently corresponded with secret (unconscious) motivations which they themselves possessed. Largely by identification, they saw themselves in the murderer's role. Occasional new "confessions" are still forthcoming, years after the crime.

This could also represent in part an unconscious seeking of punishment for disowned inner aggressiveness, or partly also a neurotic seeking of attention and notoriety, and so on. Trained law enforcement officials are aware of this phenomenon and may question a suspicious confession as thoroughly as a suspicious alibi! They have learned that both can be spurious.

The phenomenon of multiple confession can lead sometimes to rather bizarre circumstances. In a more recent case,[24] a 2-year-old boy wandered off from his mountain home.

Case 55
Multiple Confessions in Mistaken Murder

Two days after Billy's disappearance on November 21st, his grandmother was charged with murder. According to reports, she made a statement that she killed him because "he got on my nerves."

Later she retracted this statement, and in turn accused her son and daughter-in-law. Still later she insisted she didn't know what had happened to the baby. In the meantime the father made two separate confessions.

The finding of the body on November 25th, dead from exposure, climaxed a welter of "confessions" in the perplexing case. The filing of three murder charges had been successively made. These were, in order, against Billy's grandmother, 64 years old, his father, James, a 24-year-old handyman, and his mother, 18 years of age.

According to the Sheriff, the father's first signed confession said that his mother had ordered that "something be done" about Billy because he "cried and wouldn't eat his beans."

After first detailing in the original "confession" that he had smothered the baby with a handkerchief, the father had next told investigators that he and his wife, compelled by the grandmother at gunpoint, cut up the body and burned it in the open fireplace.

C. IDENTIFYING WITH THE UNDERDOG

Many individuals find themselves quite upset when they see someone picked on, maligned, or badly treated. This is likely to be especially marked when the person is in a relatively more helpless position. Thus, some people tend to be fervent sympathizers with, or ardent defenders of, the underdog. Indeed, the American people are somewhat noted for this tendency, which could have very important and interesting historical roots in the events of the 18th Century in America.

The mechanism of Identification plays a prominent role in many of these reactions. Often enough the defender is really unconsciously identifying with the victim or underdog, and thus in unwitting fashion is really defending himself.

Identification in a number of variations of this theme is not infrequently encountered in psychotherapy. The following case illustrates in condensed form a fairly non-complex instance.

Case 56
Identification with the Oppressed and Betrayed Hungarians

In January, 1956, a patient entered her therapeutic session incensed over the Russian double cross of the Hungarians, after a promise of withdrawal and self determination had been made. She spent the entire session in a powerful emotional attack upon the Russians, concurrently fervently pitying the condition of the oppressed, betrayed, and slaughtered Hungarians.

It was suggested to her that although the tenor of her reaction to all this seemed justified, its intensity appeared to indicate some deeper feeling. After this she gradually became able to see the Identification she had made with the Hungarians. The intensity of her feeling ultimately proved to be due to her own intense but more hidden inner feelings of resentment toward her parents for their partly real, and partly fancied, betrayal and ill treatment of her through a long series of incidents in earlier years.

D. EGO DEFENSE

The use of Identification as a defense against insecurity is stressed by Stevenson and Neal [22] who point out that people frequently identify with something bigger and stronger, such as a city, a church, a college, a class, a secret society, or a nation. It is felt, even though unconsciously, that in union there is strength, and some of this strength is reflected back on to the individual when he has achieved an Identification of himself with the group in question. Memberships in groups and organizations are often sought with this unconscious factor as an important one among one's motives.

Coleman [4] feels that Identification helps to ward off feelings of inferiority. Some individuals certainly get an increased sense of

160

worth by identifying themselves with a person, or a group, or an institution of illustrious standing, as they view it. When the football fan boasts "We won today," he is identifying with the group that is marked with success and that is perhaps more in public favor at the moment. He may likewise identify with a loser and suffer feelings of defeat accordingly. Further, when the individual identifies too completely with the group, his reactions and his conduct may come to lack flexibility.

Negroes felt prideful and grew in self esteem when Jackie Robinson hit a homer or, earlier, when Joe Louis was an outstanding heavyweight. There is a grim story from the days of Hitler Germany about some German Jews who had managed to escape into Holland and who were captured and marched to the local police barracks for internment. While accompanied by a squad of Dutch police, one was heard to say: "Our Nazis are much better marchers!" Despite the prejudice they had escaped, the treatment they had received, and their harrowing experiences, their pattern of identifying with their erstwhile homeland was quite strong.

Bergler [3] maintains that Identification is often a tool for solving inner conflict. Identifications take place in order to gain support in the struggle against the superego's reproaches. Bergler makes an interesting division of Identifications into "leading," that is, early childhood ones, and what he calls "misleading" ones, namely those that come after the age of five years.

E. THE PROCESS BECOMES MORE APPARENT DURING THERAPY

During the course of therapy the operation of various types of Identification become more clear to the patient. This is particularly true in the case of long-term (intensive) psychotherapy and analysis. The following excerpts from widely separated therapeutic sessions after several hundred hours of treatment indicate the awareness gained concerning the operation of the process of Identification for this particular patient.

This patient said, "For me the goal of Identification is acceptance. I identify myself with someone who is acceptable to gain a similar acceptance myself." For this patient the unconscious endeavor was to gain a position like someone else who was seen to already enjoy favor with another person or a group.

Case 57
Identification with Someone Known to already Enjoy Acceptance
". . . I have been thinking about something that happened

161

to me last night at a dinner party given by Jim's Godfather and his wife, Uncle Sam and Aunt Sally. After I had been at their house for about three hours I began to realize that I was mimicking Aunt Sally's manner of speech. She doesn't exactly stutter, it is more a hesitancy in saying certain words or a sort of stammer and although at first I feel a little uncomfortable during her pauses and then 'I mean's,' after a while I think it is quite charming. Before I can help myself I am sounding exactly like her! I hope that no one else noticed what I was doing!

". . . Often when Jim's Uncle Sam calls on the telephone he comments on the fact that I sound exactly like Jim's mother. I always express surprise but actually I am fully aware of the fact that I am in fact sounding exactly like her. She was an old girl-friend of Uncle Sam's and he always has been very fond of her. I don't mean to be aping her but I know now that I am. I like Uncle Sam and I want him to like me. In identifying myself with Jim's mother, I subconsciously slip into a true imitation. . . .

". . . This business of identification is not really new with me. As I think back over my early years in Boston, I realize that my Boston accent, originally flat, became quite broad when I changed from public to private school. Although perhaps partly a conscious effort, it was to a large extent still more part of my subconscious effort to identify myself with the group into which I had been thrown. I wanted so much to be accepted and *liked* by them. I wanted to belong. . . ."

In conclusion, the major goals of Identification are approval, acceptance, and love, with some exceptions noted. The motivation is the wish to be like the other person. What results from Identification is that there is greater approval from the self, and increased acceptance and/or love from the love-object. Self-approval can then supplement, equate, or even replace the approval of others.

8. RELATIONS OF IDENTIFICATION WITH OTHER MECHANISMS

(1) Introjection and Identification as closely allied mechanisms

The relation between Identification and Introjection has already been indicated. There are some writers who regard them as so closely allied as to be difficult to distinguish. Thus, English and Pearson [6] declare that by the process of Identification or by Introjection the child takes into itself the demands and wishes, the likes and dislikes of the significant adult. Brierley, in a personal communication, writing that Identification may be made with "good" or "bad" objects, looks upon it as a possible sequel to Introjection. Fenichel [7] states that the primitive reaction of imitating what is perceived and the oral Introjection of what is perceived belong close together. Identification, sometimes in normal psychology and often in psychopathology, gives the impression, always emphasized by Freud, of being a Regression, as if it were a secondary Identification that repeats an archaic primary one. The concept of a primary Identification, according to Fenichel, denotes that actually "putting into the mouth" and "imitation for perception's sake" are one and the same, and represent the very first relation to objects.

Taylor [23] regards Introjection as the misreading of another person's or object's qualities into oneself. According to him, it is an "overidentification" when one takes unto oneself the object's qualities. Menninger [17] regards Identification as the most frequent variety of Introjection, and the opposite of Projection. Instead of palming off our faults on to someone else, as is done by Projection, we, by Introjection, may award to ourselves their virtues, or even their faults.

Brierley refers to the connection between Identification and Introjection when she affirms that it is no longer a novelty to us to find Identification with an object that is renounced or lost, as a substitute for that very object, and Introjection of this object into the ego. Young places Identification and Projection together, regarding them as phases of an anticipatory response, in which the imagination aids in the adjustment of the individual to others. Identification, according to him, is the assuming of the qualities of others in the self, while, in reverse, Projection attributes to others one's own qualities.

Freud, giving to Introjection a role in the formation of the superego, spoke of the child's Identification with his parents as having "probably long been present." This would indicate he considered some at least to have a very early origin. Freud regards Introjection as a defense against losing an object, and says that to compensate for this loss of object, Identifications with parents which have probably long been present become greatly intensified.

Klein [11] connects Introjection, Identification, and Reparation. She looks upon the Introjection of the good object as a defense mechanism, which is associated with another important mechanism, namely that of making Reparation to the object. The ego feels impelled, by its Identification with the good object, to make Restitution for all the unconscious sadistic attacks that it has launched on that object. Such attacks especially include fantasies, plus hostile thoughts and wishes.

(2) Compensation, fantasy, symbolism, and the King David Reaction

Identification has also been held to be related to Compensation and Fantasy. Shaffer [21] holds that Identification reduces tension through the achievements of others. The child thus comes to look on the assets of his parents as his own assets, and imitates the parents through the process of Identification. Most authorities have assigned a prominent place to this process and to its major influences upon character development. An interesting exception is that of Horney, whose references to this dynamism are quite rare.

Ferenczi [8] describes Identification as the forerunner of Symbolism. He believes that it arises out of the infant's endeavor to rediscover in every object his own organs and their functioning. For him, Identification is a stage preliminary not only to symbol formation, but also to the evolution of speech and Sublimation.

The *King David Reaction* includes a combination of mechanisms: Projection, Repression, Identification, and Rationalization.

9. SUMMARY

Identification is a major mental mechanism through which an individual comes to take over feelings, traits, attitudes, or various aspects of another person. Imitation is a conscious form of Identification and bears the same relation to it as does fear to anxiety, and grief to depression. Identification may be made with "good" or "bad" objects, but is more likely to be motivated by love and respect or the desire and need for them.

Projective forms of Identification include: (a) *Sympathy* by which one feels sorrow, pity, or compassion *for* another's loss, hurt, grief, or misfortune, and (b) *Empathy* by which one has an objective awareness of another's emotional feelings and can understand them and adequately appreciate their extent. The affective form of Identification is *Compathy* which is stronger, closer, and deeper. Compathy is the close sharing of emotional feelings *with* another person. Through it one subjectively experiences the emotions of a second person with him.

Through Identification one can place oneself "in the other person's shoes." It is vital to personality development and has important personal and social values. Its extent can vary widely, from the temporary taking over of a small mannerism to the assumption of much of the role of another. Through this mechanism a child may identify with a parent, or a parent with a child. An envied person, such as a more socially successful figure, may be chosen as the object for Identification. A kind of "basking in reflected glory" can take place in conjunction with this mechanism, in the shadow of "important" people.

Identification can play a very important role in the development of character traits. *Mass Identification* is seen when a large group identifies in varying degrees with a nationally prominent figure. Identification can play a major role in the learning process.

In advertising the primary appeal lies in the basic need for the article itself. The *secondary appeal* refers to the efforts on the part of advertisers to stimulate a desire for Identification with the people who actually, or by implication use the product.

In combination with other mental mechanisms, Identification has many important uses. In the Inversion of hostility in Depression, Introjection followed by Identification with the introjected person results in outward self-depreciation and punishment.

Several types of Identifications of military life were noted and illustrated. Group Identification, and the needs leading to affiliations with groups, received brief comment. Vicarious satisfaction through Identification take place rather widely and can serve useful and constructive purposes, as well as other less personally or socially valuable ones.

The concept of the *Personal Yardstick* in basing one's assessment, expectations, and reactions to a new person upon one's experience in a past relationship is important. The margin for inaccuracy, distortion and subsequent disappointment or hurt is quite large.

Identifications in childhood are very important. These are particularly made with significant adults—especially with parents and parent-surrogates. "Like father—like son" has considerable validity. *Emotional contagion* is the compathic communication of attitudes and emotional feelings. The earliest Identifications form important precedents for later ones and for later relationships. For various reasons, childhood Identifications may be encouraged. In addition to the many purposes in seeking acceptance, one may also identify with an aggressor, as a figurative means of pulling his teeth.

165

This is another defensive operation. It helps provide a basis for certain children's games. Instances of Identification with the harsh enemy captors are reported from prisoner-of-war camps.

Misidentifications refer to the adoption of conflicting aspects or traits which lead to an uncertainty about one's role or identity. Depersonalization may follow and the background may be laid for later vulnerability to Dissociative Reactions. Identification with parents whose attitudes mirror their overconcern with health may lead to similar problems for the child. The Hysterical Personality has a considerable capacity for imitativeness and for Identification with others. This can help determine his personality development and the location and type of symptoms.

The therapist needs to be aware both of long-established and of new and developing Identifications and to help his patient secure their clarification and understanding. Interesting Identifications were noted with a real or fantasied murderer which can lead to multiple confessions, and those Identifications with the underdog were examined. Some additional relations with other mechanisms were noted.

REFERENCES

1. ALEXANDER, FRANZ (1948). *Fundamentals of Psychoanalysis,* pp. 117–128. New York; Norton.
2. ALLPORT, GORDON W. (1938). *Personality, A Psychological Interpretation,* p. 185. New York; Holt.
3. BERGLER, EDMUND (1949). *The Basic Neurosis: Oral Regression and Psychic Masochism,* pp. 84, 86. New York; Grune and Stratton.
4. COLEMAN, J. C. (1950). *Abnormal Psychology and Modern Life,* p. 629. Chicago; Scott Foresman.
5. DEARMAN, H. B. and SMITH, B. M. (1963). "Unconscious Motivation and the Polygraph Test." *Amer. J. Psychiat.,* **119,** 1017.
6. ENGLISH, O. S. and PEARSON, G. H. J. (1955). *Emotional Problems of Living,* p. 58. New York; Norton.
7. FENICHEL, OTTO (1948). *The Psychoanalytic Theory of the Neuroses,* p. 37. New York; Norton.
8. FERENCZI, S. (1950). "Introjection and Transference." In *Sex in Psychoanalysis,* pp. 96, 237. New York; Basic Books.
9. FREUD, ANNA (1954). *The Ego and the Mechanisms of Defense,* 6th ed., pp. 117–121. New York; International Universities Press.
10. KANNER, LEO (1946). *Child Psychiatry,* p. 667. Springfield; C. C. Thomas.
11. KLEIN, MELANIE (1950). *Contributions to Psychoanalysis,* pp. 258, 309. London; Hogarth.
12. KRIS, MARIANNA (1944). In *Psychoanalysis Today* (Ed. by Lorand, Sandor), p. 58. New York; International Universities Press.
13. LAUGHLIN, HENRY P. (1956). *The Neuroses in Clinical Practice,* pp. 280–1. Philadelphia; Saunders.
14. — (1956). *The Neuroses in Clinical Practice,* pp. 25, 28, 96–101, 114, 251, 279, 281, 286 (*Table 20*), 326, 717. Philadelphia; Saunders.

15. — (1955). *A Psychiatric Glossary,* 5th ed. (rev.), p. 47. Washington, D.C.; American Psychiatric Association.
16. LORAND, SANDOR (1944). *Psychoanalysis Today,* pp. 209, 211. New York; International Universities Press.
17. MENNINGER, KARL A. *The Human Mind,* p. 274. Garden City, N. J.; Garden City Publishing Co.
18. O'KELLY, L. I. and MUCKLER, F. A. (1955). *Introduction to Psychopathology,* 2nd ed., p. 104. Englewood Cliffs; Prentice-Hall.
19. ORGEL, S. (1946). *Psychiatry Today and Tomorrow,* p. 84. New York; International Universities Press.
20. SADLER, W. S. (1953). *Practice of Psychiatry,* pp. 40, 1128, St. Louis; Mosby.
21. SHAFFER, LAURANCE F. (1936). *The Psychology of Adjustment: An Objective Approach to Mental Hygiene,* pp. 161–163. Boston; Houghton Mifflin.
22. STEVENSON, GEORGE H. and NEAL, LEOLA E. (1927). *Personality and Its Deviations,* p. 101. Springfield; C. C. Thomas.
23. TAYLOR, W. S. (1954). *Dynamic and Abnormal Psychiatry,* p. 532. New York; American Book.
24. *Washington Post* (1956). A.P. story, datelined Huntington, West Virginia, November 25th.
25. YOUNG, KIMBALL (1952). *Personality and Problems of Adjustment,* 2nd ed., pp. 113–116, 118–119. New York; Appleton-Century-Crofts.

CHAPTER 5

INVERSION

*. . . the repressed feeling or urge becomes expressed as
its direct opposite . . .*

1. THE NATURE OF INVERSION

A. ADOPTION IN PSYCHIATRIC TERMINOLOGY

To invert is to turn upside down or inside out. The term
Inversion has been adopted as a noun in psychiatric terminology

to describe a number of situations. Thus we may speak of the *inversion of sleep*. This usage describes a rather specific reversal of the more usual nocturnal habits of sleeping to daytime. Similarly the term *sexual inversion* has been used to describe homosexuality; a condition in which heterosexual drives have been regarded as being inverted into homosexual ones.[6]

Freud [2] used inversion to describe a conscious kind of social dissimulation of hostile affect, which will be mentioned again shortly. Finally, inversion has been used to describe the turning of affect or emotion inward towards the self. A review of the literature reveals scattered references to these and other psychologic adaptations [3, 5, 6, 8, 9] of this term.

B. A MENTAL MECHANISM

Inversion means that something has been literally turned around or reversed. I have adopted and used the term of Inversion for some years to describe a mental mechanism which operates in this way. This concept has proved useful as a convenience in teaching and in therapy.

An intrapsychic dynamism

The operation of Inversion as an intrapsychic dynamism, while not common, can be observed with some frequency by the interested and observant student of human behavior. Let us proceed to offer a definition.

C. DEFINITION

Accordingly, for the purposes of this discussion, we may define Inversion as *a mental mechanism operating outside of conscious awareness. Through this process, a specific wish, affect, or drive which has been repressed from conscious awareness as intolerable, is inverted so as to come into subjective awareness, or to be expressed in attitudes or behavior as its direct opposite.*

In other words, in the process of Inversion a specific unacceptable and disowned (unconscious) impulse or emotion becomes directly reversed in one's conscious awareness and in its outward expression.

169

2. SOME TYPES OF INVERSION

A. THE INVERSION OF UNCONSCIOUS HOSTILITY

(1) Unconscious hostility transposed into conscious feelings and expressions of friendship and fondness

As a mental mechanism, Inversion operates automatically and unconsciously to transpose repressed impulses, desires, and emotions into their opposites, thereby permitting them to have a well-disguised outward expression. Thus, by Inversion, an unacceptable impulse toward destruction, or aggression, or hostility, can be consciously experienced in its reversed form.

Consciously unacceptable hostility may give rise through its Inversion to an outward expression of friendliness, love, or protectiveness. The reverse may also occur, as we shall see illustrated in *Case 59*. The genuineness of these may or may not be suspected by the recipient.

In the following case a long-standing non-constructive pattern of the Inversion of hostility became apparent during therapy.

Case 58
Hostility Becomes Affection in Therapy

A twenty-two-year-old divorced woman with a two-year-old child entered therapy complaining of unhappiness, several symptoms of a physiologic conversion origin, and an increasing difficulty in staying away from alcohol. A year earlier she and her husband had mutually decided that they were incompatible and that although there were few major disagreements outwardly, they would be far better apart. Since then she had been drinking more frequently. She suffered with gastric distress, headaches, insomnia, and emotional fatigue.

Some months later, as therapy progressed, the patient became more warm and friendly toward the therapist. Sessions were opened with attempts at pleasant "small talk". She brought in small gifts, gave the therapist a substantial Christmas present which was incongruous with their relationship, and insisted on paying her fees in advance. She was quite concerned about the therapist's health, as for instance when he showed signs of a minor cold. Any inquiries concerning her feelings about the therapist resulted in what amounted to protestations of gratitude and friendliness.

In her fifth month of therapy, she had a dream which

170

indicated some of her deeper feelings about treatment: "My family doctor was supposed to give a lecture on neurosis. The curtain went up and there he was—asleep and drunk! A girl tried to wake him; whereupon he turned on her and beat her savagely. I was infuriated by his actions; my faith in him was shattered."

After working with this dream, some of her less conscious but more genuine underlying angry feelings toward the therapist began to emerge. Her previous overly-affectionate behavior became less appropriate. She had unconsciously inverted a considerable amount of hostility, which to her had been intolerable, and felt consciously its opposite—a warm affection. The Inversion of her feelings taking place unconsciously was part of her automatic defensive endeavor to avoid any conscious recognition of hostility.

This had been part of a pattern of response through her life. Its self-defeat lay in its blocking of even the possibility of her learning to cope more constructively and effectively with the hostile elements in her make-up. At the same time, however, this segment of her hostility had gained some partial expression unconsciously, by frustrating the therapy, and thus the therapist. In turn, its elucidation was an important milestone in her therapeutic progress.

(2) Further elaboration or reenforcement of Repression

On the other hand, a warm and tender emotional feeling which one does not dare allow to show itself in its true colors may also through its Inversion come to be subjectively experienced as a feeling at once hostile and antagonistic. We shall see this illustrated shortly.

Unconsciously, the intent of the Inversion in either instance is to defend and to protect. In the case of the destructive impulses mentioned in the above example, these were feared partly because of superego forces and partly because of the dread danger of possible retaliation. The impulse is first denied and repressed, but beyond that, it is reversed or inverted into its opposite—a process of further defense. Herein the Inversion may be thought of as a secondary elaboration, or as a reenforcement, of the original Repression and Denial.

B. LOVE BECOMES HATE

The Inversion of love into negative feelings is not seen perhaps as frequently as the Inversion of hate into positive ones. The fol-

171

lowing cases illustrate instances of the development of this variety of the Inversion of positive emotional feelings.

Case 59
Inversion of Love into Hate

A thirty-two-year-old woman, a nurse by profession, was employed by an extremely wealthy and successful business-man for the purpose of taking care of his invalid wife. During the course of her work in their home, the employer met a young engineer who commanded his respect and admiration. The engineer made fairly regular appearances at the home for business reasons. In the course of time the nurse became very much attracted to him. They had become friendly and had enjoyed several dinner engagements together. There were some intimate relations. He had enjoyed the friendship but very much wanted their relations to remain on that level. When it became apparent to the engineer that this woman had fallen in love with him, he decided upon the necessity of not dating her again.

The realization that her love had been rejected caused great anguish for this unhappy woman. On several occasions she made tearful scenes, pleading with him not to give her up. She did not make any progress, although she continued to try for a time.

Several months later her employer's wife died. To her surprise, shortly thereafter she was asked to marry him. This she did. The man she loved continued to make his regular appearances at the home. Although she unconsciously maintained her love for him, she could no longer consciously entertain these feelings because of her marriage, in addition to her pride and his rejection. She became outwardly first quite cool to him. Later, for a time she began to believe the engineer was telling her husband about their brief but, to her, meaningful affair. She gradually developed (outwardly) an acute hatred for him, and began telling her husband stories attacking his character. When the engineer came to the home she was increasingly cold and hostile toward him.

This case can be regarded as illustrating a combination of two protectively-intended mechanisms. Originally the mechanism was Denial. It became clear to her that her love for the engineer would never be returned, but this rejection in the face of her strong positive feelings for him produced intolerable hurt and anxiety. As a result she denied her attraction and love completely on any conscious level. This Denial became partly reenforced, first by a tendency toward Projection and gradually by the Inversion of her love into hatred.

The Inversion was a further progression of the Denial. The defensive endeavor was to secure ego support, conflict resolution, protection against hurt and loss, and preservation of her newly achieved emotional *status quo*.

The following instance offers some similarities. Herein are seen the kinds of defensive patterns which can be automatically called into play in the endeavor to control intolerable sexual urges.

Case 60
Attraction into Revulsion; a Homosexual Pattern of Defense

A young homosexually-oriented male in therapy suffered with terrible conflicts. Consciously he employed every resource at his command to suppress his unacceptable urges and to ensure their control. Over a period of time we learned that unconscious forces were also at work along similar lines.

Upon several occasions he had noted great dislike toward some male acquaintance. While these reactions were seemingly unaccountable, his interest in exploring them further in his therapeutic work was most apathetic; enough so as to arouse some interest as to whether this represented a secondary defense of some existing psychologic defensive endeavor. Such proved to be the case.

During a later period this patient was discussing a troublesome attraction toward a new friend. One day, as he talked about how this troubled him and of his efforts at control, he suddenly cried, "I know what will happen now. I will gradually find things to dislike and to disapprove about him. I'll gradually come to dislike, to hate him! . . . This has happened before! This is why I've had such a revulsion for Gordon, and for Horace before that! With them I had 'forgotten' what went before—only could recall my intense feelings of revulsion toward them. . . . Now it all becomes clear. . . . This has been another defense. I didn't dare recognize these feelings before! . . ."

This patient had developed a pattern of defense which operated to deny his intense attraction toward certain male friends, and by a further defensive progression secured its Inversion into the opposite affect and attitude of active distaste or revulsion.

The foregoing case illustrates in more striking fashion what can happen far more frequently and in less noteworthy instances. Inversion can operate in partial fashion; in segments of relationships.

Many other applications may be found. Undoubtedly Inversion aids in the control of certain incestuous attractions. As such neither the attraction nor its Inversion may be remotely suspected by the person concerned or by others. In other instances, such as in certain cases of frigidity, this symptom complex may represent the defensive Inversion of quite reverse drives.

C. PATTERNS BEGIN IN CHILDHOOD

At times one may observe in children the development of patterns of Inversion. In the following instance the child was gradually adopting this process in response to needs to please parents and to ensure their approval. These kinds of childhood patterns can establish important antecedents for the kinds of defensive operations which are later unwittingly called into play in adulthood.

Case 61
Developing a Pattern of Inversion in Infancy

A three-year-old girl had certain rather typical aggressive, selfish, and possessive feelings. These were however quite actively frowned upon by her parents. These feelings caused her to insist upon close possession and control of her toys and other objects. Such possession of course was not always possible and often the parents were not at all sympathetic to the child's desires.

Anxiety was generated by the resulting conflicts. This made it attractive for the child to invert her possessive desires. At this stage, when a parent asked if he might take a coveted object, there was often an aggressive "no" at first, followed quickly by an abrupt change in the child's attitude and she would carry the object to the parent and quite graciously insist that he take it. Sometimes then she would find other objects that she thought might interest the parent and take them to him also! When the parent was through with the object the child would further carry it to her friends or to other grownups and encourage them to use it.

D. INVERSION AND SYMPTOM FORMATION

(1) Inversion in various neurotic reactions

Inversion can play a role in the development of many symptoms in various types of neuroses. At times one can observe its operation in certain cases of phobias or obsessive manifestations. It can play a role in symptom formation in any type of neurosis. It can play a role in character formation and in personality development.

In the following instance an over-developed interest in clean hands on the part of a young physician engaged in therapeutic self study had elements in it of obsessive cleanliness, compulsive hand washing, and mysophobia. This patient at one point fairly early in his therapy wrote the following somewhat intellectualized summary concerning several aspects in his case which he had partially worked out.

Case 62
Inversion of Infantile Coprophilia

"As long as I can remember I have detested having dirty hands. I wash my hands at every opportunity, or feel very uncomfortable until I am able to do so. I dislike handling door knobs, and will use my elbow to push doors open to avoid putting my hands on the door handle. The necessity of using hand rails on stairs, or handling money, leaves me uneasy 'til I can wash.

"In distinct contrast, washing my hands gives me a pleasant sensation and a feeling of well being. I like to have clean hands before I start an examination, write a letter, or have an interview. I like to wear gloves if I have to change a tire. I like to wash my hands when I am through with a job or procedure, and I like to have clean hands before I start something new.

"In reflecting on this situation during therapy I have come to see how so many of my likes and dislikes have been actually based on whether my hands will get dirty or not! In fact many of my activities and probably some of my professional aspirations were determined by this phobia of dirty hands, accompanied by its converse of a soterial interest in clean hands.* The mental mechanisms of Inversion, Displacement, and Regression have been most surely at work here.

"The basis of my phobic obsession must have had its beginnings long ago, as I've been learning, in the socially unac-

---

* A *soteria* is the converse of a phobia. Accordingly, a *phobic object* is feared and produces anxiety.

Conversely, a *soterial object* is a source of comfort and security (as in the wee tot's favorite teddy bear or blanket; for example, Linus' blanket in "Peanuts").

ceptable but instinctual drives to explore and handle feces or 'unclean' body areas. Since these activities were not acceptable, an accentuation in the opposite extreme took place, that is, the necessity to have clean hands. This was protective. It illustrates the mental mechanism of Inversion. Regression may be represented by the psychological sense of well-being that occurs when I wash my hands. This feeling must have been experienced as a child and could reflect the consequence of parental approval of being clean.

"The ultimate internal bases of emotional conflict are not known to me, at least not yet, but there is no doubt that I feel the effects of its transference to the exaggerated importance to me of having clean hands. Since I've begun to gain increased understanding about all of this, my concerns over cleanliness have gradually lessened. With further work in therapy I feel they will gradually come into still more proper perspective."

(2) Inversion as a further guard against growing awareness

In the above case also, as is far more prominent in many of the more pathologic cases of obsessive compulsive neuroses, this man's warm and loving impulses were to an extent overthreatening and dangerous. This is because there is so frequently the possibility that these feelings will be not reciprocated, but actually rejected.

(3) Unconscious defense against intolerable rejection

In these instances the person involved unconsciously defends himself against what is for him the feared repetition of an intolerable rejection that he has already experienced. Not only must he then banish it from his conscious subjective awareness, but in addition he must further unconsciously invert it into the opposite, into a conscious feeling of hostile antagonism.

The old maid, outwardly disdainful and at times openly expressing antagonism to all male creatures, may sometimes unwittingly reveal to the therapist (and to enlightened laymen) an unconscious outward façade which in its intensity points out even more clearly her warm and loving impulses and desires. These have been repressed because of the too-threatening potential for rejection, and/or for other reasons. Their subsequent further protective Inversion into their opposite followed. *Case 59* was a more specific example of defense against an intolerable rejection.

E. PHOBIC INVERSION

(1) The seeming paradox of the phobia

Inversion can be readily observed in certain types of simple phobic reactions. Here the desired object or event not only is consciously intolerable so that it is completely rejected from conscious awareness, but the emotional feelings toward and about it are, in addition, inverted, so that it becomes actually an object of fear and dread.

Through Inversion then, this becomes a further vehement conscious denial of the intolerable unconscious wish. One learns in the study of the phobias the most interesting, useful, and seemingly paradoxical fact that *what is consciously feared and dreaded* (*or what this symbolically represents*) *is also on a far less conscious level actually wanted and sought out.*[7]

(2) Inversion reenforcing Repression and control

In the following example, Inversion aided in the protective inhibition of activity in response to dangerous internal aggressive drives or urges. Herein Inversion served to reenforce repression and control. The patient developed a phobia of altercation and disagreement.

Case 63
A Phobia of Altercation; Inversion of Aggressive Impulses [6]

An athletically developed young builder, thirty-five years old, undertook therapy because of a number of problems in his marriage and in other important interpersonal relationships. Another distressing problem had been the development of anxiety in the presence of altercation, a distress so severe as to lead to a phobic kind of avoidance. He simply could not tolerate any kind of arguments or dissention.

Normally and healthily self-assertive prior to a year or so earlier, his anxious fear when conflict threatened was most distressing. Even when he was not personally concerned and could not remotely become involved himself he became most uneasy. He was very troubled by all of this, accused himself of cowardice, and often became angry with himself. As a consequence his self-esteem suffered a great deal.

In earlier years he had been normally self-assertive, with

177

a healthy Inhibition-Action Balance * in response to the aggressive part of his inner impulses. Certain great stresses had arisen however, including an almost insoluble marital conflict, to create intolerable aggressive urges. These had become of such strength as to urgently threaten a breakthrough into his conscious awareness with the dreaded possibility of action and loss of control.

Any type of controversy served to jar (however slight, it was now threatening!) a tenuous and potentially explosive internal balance. In the service of further defensive denial and control, part of the energy of the internal aggressive impulses was inverted so that any slight external suggestion of aggressiveness became feared and dreaded. The phobic kind of avoidance had gradually begun, accompanied by increased outward friendliness, a bland attitude, and overtolerance for others. Aggressive tendencies, now greatly feared, had become inverted, including even their normal and healthy self-assertive components.

(3) The Inversion of an intolerable wish into a phobic dread

In another interesting case reported earlier,[6] a patient suffered from an obsessive phobic dread of his wife becoming insane. Ultimately we discovered that the symptom represented the Inversion into consciousness of its opposite! His unconscious wish had actually been for his wife *to become* insane.

This patient had unconsciously longed for escape from an unhappy marriage. This had been intolerable to him and hence repressed. In this instance as in others in which Inversion has been employed, the desired object or event was not only consciously intolerable and hence rejected entirely from conscious awareness, but it was additionally *inverted* to become an object of fear and dread. This progression illustrates the important concept which I have called the *Secondary Defense*. In this significant and frequent sequence, the manifestation—a defense in itself—is in turn, i.e., secondarily defended (*see* references, pages 15–16, 190–91, and 241).

---

* The Inhibition-Action Balance [6] refers to *the relative balance maintained by every individual between his subjective experiencing of emotional feelings, and his outward behavior in the response to them.* This is conceived as being in response to an individual's unconscious aggressive drives, his loving drives, and so on, and all the related impulses.

The assessment of this important balance and its relative stability can be used as a further index to an appraisal of the present and potential level of the emotional health of a person.

This is a further defense against the intolerable unconscious wish. Inversion can contribute to the development of a phobia, or phobia-like symptoms. The case of mysophobia (*Case 62,* preceding) also helps illustrate this.

3. ATTITUDES, MEMORY, GOALS, AND STANDARDS

A. THE INVERSION OF ATTITUDES

(1) An efficient, specific, and direct reversal of attitude

Inversion is a more efficient mechanism than Reaction Formation in the sense that it affects primarily one impulse or drive, not a whole constellation. It is a mechanism operating outside of and beyond conscious awareness in which a *specific* and more or less discrete wish, impulse, affect, or drive which is intolerable and thereby disowned is directly reversed. It can operate in many areas, as in both the conscious and unconscious Inversion of attitudes.

(2) A conscious kind of social Inversion

Freud used the term "inversion" to describe a conscious and deliberate kind of *social* inversion in which there is a reversal of the attitudes which are outwardly expressed towards another person. In an example which Freud gave, the inversion of the outwardly expressed attitudes was achieved simply by conscious effort. This is a kind of social dissimulation that is employed fairly frequently. To varying degrees in social situations, people conceal and invert their true feelings in whole or in part.

Freud noted further, "If I am conversing with a person to whom I must show consideration while I should like to address him as an enemy, it is almost more important that I should conceal the expression of my affect from him than that I should modify the verbal expression of my thoughts." [3]

At times in this conscious endeavor of concealment and denial, the outward expression is a complete inversion of what is genuinely felt. Distaste or dislike may be masked by outward warmth and friendliness. More rarely perhaps, affection and fondness may be disguised by a display of aloofness, coolness, or even hostility. These are *conscious* efforts.

It is not difficult, however, for us to understand that similar developments can take place which are completely unconscious. The differences may be more those of level of awareness or complexity, rather than of differences in kind.

(3) Familial Inversion of attitudes

The following case, cited very briefly, is an example of an unconscious Inversion of attitude towards a sibling. This kind of attitudinal Inversion towards a close relative may occasionally be encountered clinically.

Case 64
Inversion of Attitudes Toward an Older Sibling

A young man in therapy had an older brother who had always been very much the one favored by their parents. Jim could never consciously own his deep resentment and hatred of his brother, it being far too distasteful a reaction and contrary to our usual mores. Instead he had always professed great love and admiration for his brother.

There were other areas which were sources for envious resentment. For example, he was particularly envious of his brother's superior ability in sports. But instead of being able to admit this realistically and honestly to himself, through the unconscious operation of the mechanism of Inversion, he went out of his way to praise his brother's outstanding ability in this field. This he would do to the point of boredom on occasion and to persons who had not the slightest interest.

It was not surprising perhaps that their relationship was not at all close despite the Inversion. After this young man came to recognize his underlying feelings more clearly, to accept and to examine them, they became far less a problem. The great need for their control diminished. The two brothers began to get along together far better.

(4) The Inversion of parental attitudes

Many attitudes may be inverted, to be thus transformed into their opposites. The rejection and hatred of a child may be repressed as intolerable and be experienced—and expressed outwardly—as "love". More frequently a parent may unconsciously defend against unacceptable resentful feelings toward a child by protectiveness, or by overprotectiveness.

180

Occasionally an adult may overdo his seeming affection for children. Through its very intensity or by virtue of subtle indications to the contrary it may become suspect. One may surmise the defensive operation of Inversion in some instances.

Inversion sometimes operates in the attitudes of a child toward a long-domineering and overly demanding parent. The operation of this mechanism can help bring about the lifelong type of relationship in which a child has come to devote himself more or less completely to a parent, in place of living his own life.

B. INVERSION OF MEMORY; THE WHITE-WASHING OPERATION

One of the defensive operations which we observe taking place in regard to memories is the Inversion of distasteful or troubling ones. By this means a source of possible distress can become one which is in various ways satisfying or ego building. In this kind of operation, Inversion sometimes performs a service akin to the mental mechanism of Retrospective Devaluation,[6] in which it might be viewed as a further progression.

The following instance is one in which memories have been inverted into their reverse. It is one kind of what I have come to term the *white-washing* operation. This occurs not infrequently in less striking examples.

Case 65
White-Washing: A Process of the Retrospective Denial and Inversion of Memories

This instance concerns a woman now eighty-seven years of age whom I have known for many years. Since the age of sixty-seven years she has been widowed. During the many decades of her married life, Tom had never been what one would call an exceptionally good husband. Far from it, he was a pretty miserable failure at holding up anywhere near his end of the marital partnership. During these years his wife had not been particularly timorous about remarking on his failures. He had done "a poor job as a father," had given up several good positions to the detriment of the family, was occasionally abusive with little objective basis, and "drank too much."

Now, for some years following his death, all unpleasant memories have been denied. Many memories have become inverted. She has now come to remember her husband quite sincerely as "the best husband one could possibly have." He is remembered as a thoughtful and kind man. Her recollections having been inverted, now serve as a source of pleasure and satisfaction to her.

C. INVERSION OF GOALS AND STANDARDS

(1) Blocking of a goal leading to Inversion

Attitudes may become inverted for a number of reasons. An important basis for the Inversion of an attitude may be found sometimes in frustration; for example in the blocking of a cherished goal. When such an event occurs, other things which had not seemed important heretofore may rapidly become so, while interest is similarly lost in the areas which have been blocked. These areas may be opposite or reversed, representing an Inversion of goals. The new goal is also quite likely a Compensation.

The following instance is a fairly superficial but not uncommon example, in which this development occurred in a young adult. This kind of operation can be a very important psychologic defense.

Case 66
A "Sports-Oriented" Collegian Becomes "Study-Oriented"

F. K. was a twenty-four-year-old senior medical student who was an excellent scholar and one of the leading students in his class. This had not always been the case.

During his early college days he had had only one strong desire—"to be a varsity football player." This was a cherished goal from his early years. Although his skill was rather mediocre, he worked very hard at the sport—to the extent that both his scholastic and social life suffered. Several times he was called before the Dean because of his dismal showing in the classroom. Despite his quite limited ability in football, his great efforts finally succeeded in his gaining a second string berth on the team in his sophomore year, against a great deal of competition. This considerable measure of success seemingly cemented his sports orientation in college.

In September of his junior year, however, he suddenly found his position being completely dominated by a freshman! Another freshman was almost equally promising. His goal in football was quite effectively blocked.

F. K. quit the team. He seemed almost instantaneously to have lost all his prior interest in football and simultaneously most of his interest in all kinds of outdoor activity. From sports-oriented he became study-oriented. His disinterest in academic work was inverted into studiousness.

This was accomplished so successfully that he had been able through most diligent application the next year to compile an almost phenomenal straight A average. The loss of his original goal was so rapidly followed by its replacement through the Inversion of his frustrated sports-interest attitudes, that what might have been a psychologic tidal wave was only a ripple. It had been a very effective defensive operation.

(2) The Inversion of standards of morality and conduct

Occasionally one may encounter instances of the Inversion of one's standards in some major area. The following is a striking and major example in which a stringent attitude about morals and sexuality became inverted into its reverse, with a resulting series of openly conducted affairs.

Case 67
Inversion of Standards of Sexual Behavior

An attractive and well-to-do divorcee was referred for psychotherapy by her physician because of handicapping personality traits and some general dissatisfaction with her life. Early in the treatment her rather promiscuous sexual behavior came to light. She asserted that incidents of this nature caused her no problems. She ruled out the presence of any resulting emotional conflicts and vetoed further discussion.

Nonetheless we gradually secured more data about this area of her living while concentrating more specifically upon others. It appeared that her affairs were conducted rather blatantly. She had a kind of flagrant disregard of her friends' criticisms on repeated occasions and seemed to almost invite their attention to her sexual adventures. Her flaunting attitude conveyed to them her contempt for their "prudishness" and "narrow viewpoints." Still it appeared clear that fifteen years earlier, prior to her marriage and divorce, her own views had, if anything, been considerably more stringent than those of her friends.

During these emotionally stormy years her standards of sexual behavior had been inverted. Entering into the dynamics were elements of defiance, hostility, and disillusionment, plus contributing assists from the mechanisms of Denial and Rationalization. The Inversion allowed her certain neurotic gratifications for which, however, she also paid in other ways. The effects of an underlying rather strict superego while no longer effective in controlling her behavior, exacted a more devious toll unconsciously.

During the course of therapy the elucidation of her psychologic endeavors of Repression, Denial, and Inversion gradually led to a reinstatement of more socially approved standards of behavior. These came to be on a more sound and rational basis, however, than in her earlier years.

(3) Aspects of living, character traits, money management and suspicion

Inversions may occur similarly in various aspects of living. Character and personality changes result which may be major or minor. The new trait or characteristic often enough is "intended" as a defense against that which it replaces. Thus the Inversion in the preceding case may be regarded as an attempted defense against that part of the patient's conscience which would overinhibit.

The overly cautious person in matters of money management may have inverted his real underlying feared and disowned spend-thrift tendencies as a rigorous endeavor in their control. Through Inversion a miserly person may become overgenerous as a defense against his disowned and overdeveloped needs to hoard money. Suspiciousness may develop as an attempted defense against one's naïveté and *vice versa*.

4. INVERSION AND OTHER MECHANISMS

A. INVERSION AND REACTION FORMATION

(1) Similarity of results

The defensively intended mechanisms of Inversion and Reaction Formation have a certain relationship despite other distinctions which can be made. Most important is that the end result of these unconscious psychologic endeavors is similar. Further, both represent emotional reversals which are automatic, unconscious, and without any conscious effort on the part of the individual. Needless to say the drawing of any absolute lines of demarcation between the mechanisms of Inversion, Reaction Formation, and Reversal may accordingly be a difficult matter, or even an arbitrary one.

(2) Criteria in the delineation of Inversion and Reaction Formation

We can, however, note certain general criteria in delineating Inversion from Reaction Formation. Inversion differs from Reaction Formation in: (*a*) that it is relatively specific, (*b*) that it is more immediate, (*c*) that it usually functions within narrower limits, and (*d*) that there are, in it, less frequent involvements of ego machinations over any considerable period of time in its development. Generally, Reaction Formation involves a series of related attributes or attitudes, while Inversion is likely to have a more limited application to a specific idea or feeling.

Inversion does not usually reflect so much of the long-term characterologic developmental process which is more implicit to the operation of Reaction Formation,[1] although this is variable. Reaction Formation is known as a "reaction of the opposite." It is likely to involve large areas of the personality. Inversion is a direct and more isolated "turning around" or reversal, of the specific discrete original impulses or wish. Inversion by definition is nearly 100 per cent effective in its more narrow area; Reaction Formation is effective in varying degrees and seldom is so completely effective in the degree of direct reversal which takes place.

B. REPRESSION IS REENFORCED; A PROGRESSION BEYOND DENIAL

Inversion, like other defense mechanisms, technically cannot stand by itself. For a feeling or a wish or a complex to be inverted, it must first be repressed. In consequence, there is a consciously unconscious one. For example, conscious feelings of disgust, vociferously expressed, may take the place of disowned feelings of pleasure. By the use of Inversion, the Repression is reenforced. The original feeling has not only become disowned (repressed), but it remains hidden from conscious awareness.

This progression of events goes beyond Denial, as discussed earlier, and in which the disowned feeling is merely denied. By the use of Inversion, Denial not only takes place, but the feelings are further disguised so that the concealment from conscious awareness (and the sought after escape from the anxiety which this would occasion) is reenforced. What is finally allowed conscious expression has been inverted into the exact opposite of the intolerable affect, which remains unconscious.

C. INTROJECTION, DEPRESSION, REGRESSION, NARCISSISM

The term inversion is also used, psychologically as noted, to describe the turning inward toward the self of affects which were originally and unconsciously directed toward others. In this type of use it is somewhat akin and is often used in conjunction with the mental mechanism of Introjection.

These two terms we also find used in discussing the psychologic handling of the consciously unacceptable aggression which is present in Depression. Accordingly, in the depressed patient, one may speak of the Inversion of his hostile-aggressive impulses. This use of the term is quite proper, even though it must be recognized that this simplified description short circuits several steps in the dynamic course of events, which is actually more complex. This kind of inversion is a turning against the self, and involves not only the unconscious effect of Introjection, but also Identification. As a result, the hostile feelings are inverted, or turned against the self.

From the foregoing we have recognized another major concept in which the term of Inversion is employed as concerns the turning inward of otherwise intolerable impulses and drives. There are other illustrations of this. For example, in certain cases in which narcissism is a prominent feature, love has become inverted from others towards the self. In such instances it may have seemed safer to turn one's love impulses back toward the self.

This is a tragically self-defeating kind of attempted solution. It may be undertaken rather than to risk the dangers of a more mature relationship. A close relationship had too many inherent dangerous potentials for rejection and loss. This development is sometimes encountered in regressive (or secondary) kinds of narcissism.

D. DISTORTION AND INVERSION

We have observed Inversion operate in multiple areas. These have included the inversion of specific disowned thoughts, intent, attitudes, aims and goals. Another important area is that involved in one's interpretation of the attitudes and behavior of another person.

In this type of usage Inversion becomes a major type of Distortion of one's evaluation. This proved to be the case in the following instance.

186

Case 68
The Inversion of the Therapist's Role by the Patient; a Distortion Occurs in Therapy

A patient with certain handicapping obsessive character traits had entered therapy because of his desire to secure constructive changes in these. From time to time in one or another of his treatment sessions there would be an occasional incoming phone call. My usual response whenever possible was to politely but promptly indicate I was not free to talk, to secure a number, and arrange to call back later.

My patient just as regularly inverted my role in these instances from a passive one to an active one. He resented the calls a great deal. He complained about them often and at great length. He repeatedly also thought and spoke of the calls as having been *initiated by me*. Thus, he would say, "When you made that call . . .," "the phone call you just made . . .," "that call you made on Tuesday . . ." and so on. To him I was the active party. Pointing out a distinction made little difference. He could recognize this on an intellectual level but every time he spoke at all spontaneously about the calls, any reference to them made me the caller. This Inversion of my role continued for *years*.

To have actually made such calls while he was telling me of important events and during a period set aside for him would have indeed been a flagrant disregard of his interests. It would have constituted a very contemptuous treatment of his seeking help and of his efforts to communicate. Eventually seeing me in just such an unfavorable light proved to have been the major aim of this entire unconscious operation. This was an anti-therapeutic maneuver which however reflected the negative part of his transference. It was urgently required to help him maintain distance; the dangers inherent in a close relationship were too threatening.

Accordingly, he preserved his distance and relative emotional isolation in a defensive fashion through various distortions about his therapist and the latter's supposed attitudes and behavior toward him. Among these "endeavors," unconsciously motivated, the Inversion of my role in the phone calls, from being a passive recipient to that of the person initiating the calls, was an interesting illustration.

The importance of the above Inversion as a psychologic defense is amply demonstrated in the persistence and tenacity with which it was maintained and in the length of its duration. It did not give way easily to mere logic or reason. It was an emotionally determined part of his unconscious defenses.

Thus, pointing out the Inversion on some of the more suitable occasions, plus the patient's conscious recognition—literally for years—that he was thus tricking himself, made only a very gradual inroad upon this particular defensive operation. Even after his attitudes had undergone considerable modification, at least on a conscious level, an occasional slip of the tongue betrayed lingering subconscious remnants.

E. RATIONALIZATION AND INVERSION: ENHANCING THE SELF PICTURE; THE PRINCIPLE OF THE PERSONAL YARDSTICK

(1) The maintenance of an acceptable self-picture

Rationalization is an important defense mechanism which is frequently employed to maintain an acceptable self picture in the interpretation of a person's own attitudes and behavior. At times a complete Inversion takes place in the development of this kind of vital unconscious defensive endeavor.

In the following briefly cited instance the patient thoroughly believed that he was behaving "nobly," that he was "doing good" and serving as a "benefactor" while conducting a destructive affair with his best friend's wife. It was absolutely intolerable at the time, in the face of his high personal standards, to consciously recognize the destructive implications which were present, through a more objective appraisal of his conduct.

Case 69
Destructive into Noble; Inversion in Maintaining an Acceptable Self Picture

A young engineer in therapy became involved in an affair with the wife of his best friend, unbeknown to the latter. Consciously he saw himself only as "doing good." He maintained to himself and to me that his motivation was in providing (selflessly) necessary warmth and affection. This his friend wouldn't provide, and therefore he was "holding the marriage together."

He absolutely had to see himself as doing good in every situation, especially in this affair. It was more true in this situation since he was not measuring up at all to his standards. He was their "benefactor." Several instances of pedophiliac sex play with their six-year-old daughter were also rationalized on the basis that of course the child "couldn't possibly know what was going on anyway."

Unconsciously his judgments were of a quite different

order. Ultimately his Rationalizations lost their potency and we learned of his really overly strict moral judgments, which in addition had had to be kept submerged in order to permit the neurotic gratifications he sought.

The Inversion of what was destructive into something which he consciously viewed as noble had for a time allowed him to continue his otherwise personally intolerable behavior. Shunted aside had been his very strict moralistic and judgmental self assessments of "criminal," "detestable," "immoral," "deceitful," and so on, which through gradual working out and derepression we eventually learned.

(2) Inversion and Rationalization enhancing the self evaluation

The following is a somewhat similar instance. A patient's virtuous self picture was also maintained by a rationalized Inversion. On later study we learned that this patient had repressed a harsh and adjudging superego.

Case 70
Maintaining a Virtuous Self Picture

A thirty-eight-year-old bachelor had not been able to marry although his history revealed a series of close relationships with women. These however had tended to follow a rather definite pattern.

A long period of quite platonic friendship would very, very slowly and gradually lead into a love affair, after which he lost interest rather abruptly until a new prospect was selected. His latest friend was a terribly shy and virtuous girl for whom no effort was too great for him to make in order to try and please her. He performed myriad small services for her. He devoted tremendous conscious efforts to help her and to make himself useful.

The patient thought of himself consciously as a wonderful guy—and so did she! Such devotion, such kindness, such thoughtfulness! However, it ultimately became clear that his real and sole aim was seduction. This was another conquest.

He suffered from a modified and less obvious kind of Don Juanism.[4] The selflessness was a sham and a means to an end. This was such a consciously intolerable and repugnant picture of himself however, that it had become defensively inverted to conceal from himself his truly quite selfish aims and to maintain his self esteem. Much later his evaluation of this as one of his series of relationships was much different.

"It was prostitution. Rather than induce her to give me

herself for money—unthinkable for her—I plied her with 'good deeds,' gifts, services, favors, kind treatment and help-fulness. . . . It was really all just a long-range campaign of seduction . . . calculated too, although I couldn't and wouldn't see it before. . . ."

(3) The personal yardstick

In the foregoing two cases important Distortions have been facilitated in maintaining or building up the self evaluation or self picture. It must be recognized that similar Inversions can take place in one's appraisal of others—their attitudes, standards, attributes. This is in accord with the principle of the Personal Yardstick.*

F. DISTORTIONS IN MARITAL CONFLICT; THE CONCEPT OF SECONDARY DEFENSE

(1) Inverted evaluations of others

At first glance it might seem surprising that some of the more noteworthy of these inverted and distorted pictures of others are likely to develop in one's appraisal of those who are closest. Thus, important ones may be uncovered in the detailed study of cases of marital conflict. Distortions of the evaluation of a spouse are not uncommon and develop for several noteworthy psychologic needs (for example: idealization, carry-overs of past relationships, experiences, and patterns from childhood; Projection, and so on). Their degree and extent may well reflect their level of psychologic import and this in direct proportion.

(2) Inversion as a Secondary Defense

Inversion as a direct reversal is thus likely to reflect a con-siderable amount of underlying unconscious need. Accordingly it may be uncovered with great difficulty and clung to most tena-ciously. This again illustrates our concept of the *Secondary Defense.*

---

* The principle of the Personal Yardstick *is the use of the self as a "yardstick" in the appraisal, estimation, evaluation, and prediction of an-other's feelings, attitudes or behavior.*

Subject to wide variations as to accuracy it is nonetheless a vital measuring device and often the only one available or employed. Tremen-dous individual differences exist in its frequency of employment and in its accuracy.

This is a very important and useful concept. In it *the symptom, a defense in itself, is in turn* (that is secondarily) *defended.*

The patient has unconsciously elaborated a defensive symptom, characteristic, complex, or mechanism because of desperate internal needs. Regardless of how handicapping or self defeating it may be from an objective standpoint, it is clung to tenaciously.

This is the primary defense. Its defense in turn is the secondary defense *by* the patient *of* the prior defense. Since this defense follows (and defends) a prior one, I have assigned it the descriptive name of *secondary defense.*

Patients cling desperately to their symptoms. An understanding of this important concept helps one understand better the requisite length and the great complexity of the work of treatment. The resistances encountered in psychotherapy and analysis are often illustrative of very effective and tenacious types of secondary defense.

G. OTHER RELATIONSHIPS OF INVERSION

Inversion can also be a way of Undoing. It is a type of Reversal as noted earlier. Also as noted before, it serves to reenforce Repression and can represent a further progression beyond Denial. In Denial, the disowned feeling, impulse, or wish is simply denied to any conscious awareness. The reversal of Inversion is an additional step intended to supplement the concealment.

Inversion may at times be regarded as another form of the psychologic defense of overcompensation. Its similarity to Compensation [1] was also illustrated in *Case 65.* Inversion is illustrated in certain simple cases of Projection—for example, the child who unconsciously turns around (that is, *inverts*) the feeling of "I would like to hit him" into one of "He wants to hit me."

5. INVERSION CAN HAVE IMPORTANCE IN CHARACTER TRAIT DEVELOPMENT

A. THE DEPRESSIVE PERSONALITY

Character (personality) traits may be influenced by Inversion. This can be observed in their various constellations. Among these, it can be demonstrated rather readily in the depressive type of personality. In this group the character traits often result at least partly from an Inversion of hostile and aggressive impulses. This is illustrated in the following extract of a case.

Case 71

Inversion of Hostile and Aggressive Impulses in Character Trait Development

A thirty-one-year-old patient was mild-mannered, overly polite, quite serious in mien, and very compliant. He presented an overdevelopment of the depressive group of character traits. He was rather typically inclined to moroseness and low spirits, and was overly concerned with detail. Maintaining perfectionistic standards, and with an overdeveloped conscience, he carried too great a burden of responsibility. He was the victim of his own harsh conscience. He had gradually taken over the highly critical attitudes toward himself, of his stern and adjudging parents.

As might have been expected, he required considerable satisfactions from outside himself, in view of early realistic deprivations of love and acceptance, and a deficiency in internal sources of supply. In his interpersonal relationships one could find evidences of his terribly strong (but deeply unconscious) needs for acceptance and love.

Another typical psychologic element was the presence of strongly mixed or ambivalent feelings, again wholly outside of and beyond his conscious awareness. There was a great amount of aggression present which had been generated in response to the early deprivations of his childhood. This had seemed too dangerous to tolerate. Consequently it had quickly and automatically been repressed from all conscious awareness. Here we see an antecedent pattern for this man's future reactions so that most of his later hostile feelings were similarly repressed.

As a result of extensive psychotherapy, this man gradually became able to effect an internal readjustment of harsh and punishing superego forces. His defensive character traits had earlier developed in the service of Repression and Denial. Although he was inwardly torn by hostile feelings, outwardly he was calm, mild-mannered, and compliant. Thus he outwardly denied to the world as well as to himself, the presence of his very considerable pent-up but unconscious hostility.

Originally, his automatic rejection from consciousness of his hostile feelings in childhood had been based on a feared and dreaded retaliation from his stern parents. Further, the danger of harboring destructive aims toward these vitally necessary objects of his own dependence was too great. As part of the desperate protection against awareness, his hostile impulses toward people were inverted. Traits developed which were quite opposite to his hidden feelings, an important part of his psychologic defenses.

It required long and extensive treatment to bring this man to an insight into the forces at work within him.

B. IN OBSESSIVE AND HYPOCHONDRIACAL TRAITS

Inversions of aggressive impulses can contribute in another application of the term to the obsessive group of personality traits. In the analysis (reported before [6]) of a case of character neurosis of this type, the patient was a highly self-critical individual. During therapy, this proved to be partly a direct reflection of his harsh, overdeveloped conscience, that is, of his superego, and partly an inversion of hidden, disowned aggressive and punitive attitudes toward others.

In another case * it became apparent in the course of analytic work that a series of episodic hypochondriacal attacks occurred whenever strong destructive tendencies or aggressive-hostile feelings were being forced into awareness. This patient's character structure had been developed to ward off the recognition of such aspects of the self. Any event of life that provoked such feelings came to be experienced as a dreaded threat.

The hypochondriacal attacks that would follow served to turn the threatening feelings away from the outward object or person, and inward toward the self. This involved the operation of the mechanism of Introjection together with this type of inversion.

6. THE INVERSION OF MOOD

A. DEPRESSION INTO ELATION

(1) The large cyclic swing in spirits

An interesting and important application of some of the principles of Inversion is encountered occasionally in the area of mood and mood swings. As with an emotion, the reversal of a mood can sometimes take place quickly; rarely even dramatically, in the absence of an apparently sufficient external basis. The more this is reflected in behavior, demeanor, etc., the more noteworthy it will be.

The most marked examples of mood Inversion, however, are to be found clinically in those emotional illnesses which are characterized by large cyclic swings in spirits. Our discussion requires

---

* Ref. 6, Case 183.

such an illustration. Accordingly, the following interesting example is offered. In considering it, it should be noted carefully that only by having known this person over a span of time could one have been aware of the Inversion, even though it was so major in extent.

(2) A clinical instance

To see this patient at one pole or the other—with each maintained over a period of time—would offer an observer little hint necessarily of the marked change possible from one to the other. These changes took place quite gradually but effected a complete transition in the patient, as we shall see.

Case 72

Depression into Elation: A Major Inversion of Mood

A twenty-four-year-old teacher was in treatment because of the onset of a severe Depressive Reaction which had temporarily ended her effectiveness at work. In October, after four months of therapy, she was still quite ill. She appeared dejected, sad, and morose. She had nearly abandoned all social life and suffered from terrible self-consciousness. To escape contacts with people she went to many movies or roamed about on long solitary walks, often at night. She was molested several times and possibly narrowly escaped more serious consequences. Hiking along the canal or river bank she ruminated about suicide. Her determination to continue in therapy was only partially reassuring in this regard, since her commitment to this was sometimes quite tenuous.

She shared an apartment with her sister. She was so desperately shy that she avoided meeting the latter's callers. On one occasion for example she "hid" in the bedroom and used some chinaware as a urinary receptacle when necessary, to keep from having to visit the bathroom. Her appearance and manner were such as to repel most people. Only one or two faithful friends managed to continue to occasionally seek her out in the face of her unresponsiveness and withdrawal.

By April all this had changed completely. In the space of just a few months she had undergone a complete metamorphosis. The transformation was nearly unbelievable. If one had not seen her during this period, he could hardly have recognized the radiant, vivacious, and attractive butterfly who had now emerged from her cocoon of depression.

In mood, appearance, and behavior everything was oppo-

194

site. She had reversed moroseness into gaiety, somberness into lightheartedness, shyness into confidence and boldness, dull and ponderous mental activity into that which was both facile and witty. The once so backward, unattractive, frightened, and sad little mouse had blossomed out so much that now she hardly thought twice about flirting mischievously with an older married man. From dowdy she had become beautiful; from friendless to having a host of friends who grew steadily and rapidly in number.

Her relations with her parents were also reversed. Previously she constantly and bitterly complained about them and avoided them. Now everything was rosy—too much so—since her glossing over points of conflict was another evidence of a new defense, one of superficiality. From depressed she had become elated in mood; a major Inversion. It was fascinating to observe the change. This took place unwittingly, unconsciously, inexorably; brought about by powerful intrapsychic forces.

Was the changed girl still ill? By many of our social standards her adjustment would have been rated as quite superior. Her elation was more marked in a relative sense to her prior state, rather than as a symptom which might set her apart. Socially, it was well within bounds. Still, given the opportunity, the careful clinician might have found a number of indications which would have led him to consider her very much in need of therapy.

(3) Deficient insight: a danger signal

First, there was the considerable likelihood of another depression. She had suffered a prior milder one earlier. Secondly, her insight was if anything more defective than previously. Finally, there were other personality features, including for example, such items as her superficiality, her glossing over problems, her non-awareness of others' feelings or sensitivities, her impatience, the rapid sequence of thoughts which prevented thorough attention to most items, and the brittleness of her usually high spirits.

Everything was "fine" she believed. What need was there to continue therapy? "I don't want to even remember how things were six months ago! . . ." (nor again when she had been depressed 18 months previous to the present episode!). In many respects she was a far less ideal candidate for therapy following the major mood Inversion than formerly.

7. SUMMARY

Inversion is employed to name several concepts in modern dynamic psychiatry. These include the inversion of heterosexual orientation, inversion of sleep habits, inversion of feelings in their social expression, and the inversion of aggressive impulses in depression. In the foregoing discussion we have stressed its employment as a mental mechanism. The concept of Inversion finds its most important utilization in the latter.

A mechanism which is outside of conscious awareness, Inversion operates automatically and with defensive intent to specifically and directly reverse an intolerable impulse or wish so that it becomes consciously experienced thus. It is an important intrapsychic defensive endeavor.

We have observed how hostility may be inverted into affection and love into hate. Patterns of Inversion may begin in infancy and may be found also in the later years of life. Inversion can play a role in the development of many symptoms of the neuroses such as phobias, obsessions, and overconcern with health (hygeiaphrontis). Attitudes may become inverted. Memories may become inverted. Goals may become inverted.

Inversion operates in conjunction with other mental mechanisms, especially Repression and sometimes Introjection, Identification, Projection, Distortion, and Rationalization. It can represent a further step beyond Denial. Inversion is one major kind of Reversal. Inversion can also represent an overcompensation. The end results are similar to Reaction Formation, from which distinctions have been made.

The role of Inversion has been noted in maintaining or enhancing an acceptable self-picture, as has been a similar contribution to the influencing of one's evaluation of others. The important and useful concepts of the *Personal Yardstick* and the *Secondary Defense* have been cited.

Inversion enters into the important area of character trait development of various types. Finally, the Inversion of mood was cited. This is most marked clinically in cases of emotional illness characterized by major cyclic mood swings. A number of illustrations have been cited from clinical experience.

REFERENCES

1. BRIERLY, MARJORIE (1959). Personal communication.
2. FREUD, SIGMUND (1933). *The Interpretations of Dreams.* 3rd ed. Translated by Brill, A. A. New York; Macmillan.

3. HINSIE, L. E. and SHATZKY, J. (1953). *Psychiatric Dictionary*. 2nd ed. New York; Oxford.
4. LAUGHLIN, HENRY P. (1959). "The Mental Mechanisms: Compensation." *Bull. Mont. Co. Med. Soc.,* **3**(10), .
5. — (1959). "The Mental Mechanisms." *Bull. Mont. Co. Med. Soc.,* **3**(9), .
6. — (1956). *The Neuroses in Clinical Practice.* Pp. 72–77, 106–109, 121–122; *Case 80,* p. 184; 198–207, 423, 466–467, 717; *Case 139,* p. 387; *Case 138,* p. 524; p. 525, 576, 610, 718, 720, 739. Philadelphia, Saunders.
7. — (1956) *Ibid.,* pp. 152–220
8. — (1954). "Fear and Phobias" Part 1. *Med. Ann. D.C.,* **23**, 379.
9. MENNINGER, KARL A. (1930). *The Human Mind,* p. 282. Garden City, N. J.; Garden City Publishing Co.

CHAPTER 6

COMPENSATION

. . . making up for realistic, or subjectively evaluated deficiencies . . .

1. THE NATURE OF COMPENSATION

A. DEFINITION

Compensation is *a mental mechanism operating outside of and beyond conscious awareness through which a person seeks to offset, to make up for, or to "compensate" for his deficiencies or defects.* Such deficiencies may be quite real, or may be fancied to varying degrees. They may relate to nearly any area of living. Included are such personally important things as one's skills, attributes, behavior, character traits, performance, physique, handicaps from illness, or aspects of personality.

Compensation represents an unconscious attempt to meet certain standards, which are likely to be self-imposed because of some area of actual or supposed inferiority. The major underlying bases for Compensation lie in the desire to secure ego reenforcement; attention, conflict resolution, recognition, approval, acceptance, or love. These may be sought from aspects of one's self, from others, or from both.

B. A MAJOR EGO DEFENSE

Like other psychologic defense mechanisms, Compensation is an unconscious endeavor in the service of conflict resolution, the reduction of tensions, and the warding off of anxiety.[2] According to Coleman,[1] Compensation is the ego defense mechanism through which an undesirable trait is covered up by the exaggeration of a desirable one. By its use one conceals a weakness by developing a desirable trait, or makes up for frustration in one area by gratification in some other. As O'Kelly and Muckler[6] regard this intrapsychic defense mechanism, a deficit in one area of personality (as subjectively experienced) is made up for by the unconscious compensatory development of another area. Thorpe and Katz[10] see in it the effort to offset a weakness or limitation by a favorable or strong characteristic.

Most authorities hold similar views as to the definition of Compensation and as to the defensive purposes it is intended to serve. It is one of the major ego defenses or dynamisms.

C. WIDESPREAD EMPLOYMENT AND RECOGNITION

The mental mechanism of Compensation is more readily understandable to many people than are some of the other mechanisms of defense. This is partly because it is quite common for conscious efforts to be made at Compensation. I think these kinds of efforts also offer us evidence as to its widespread—nearly universal—employment. It is not difficult to carry over from a concept of effortful and conscious attempts at Compensation, to the unconscious operation of a similar endeavor as an intrapsychic defensive operation.

While many instances in which Compensation is operative are reasonably simple, its employment can run the gamut to become at times complex, quite subtle, and very elusive of analysis. Compensation follows a subjective assessment of inferiority which may or may not be based upon realistic factors as evaluated objectively and independently. Let us now consider some of the different types of Compensation.

2. TYPES OF COMPENSATION

A. FOR STATURE

(1) Personal compensation

Physical endowment as to size, which is to some degree less than average, or more than average, is a major source of concern to many people. Resulting handicaps may be more or less realistically assessed. They may also become the focus in symbolic fashion as replacements for more hidden and subjectively disavowed characterologic features.

In any event, Compensation for small or large stature, or for many other kinds of real or fancied physical deficiencies, is one of the most frequent bases for the employment of this major mechanism. At times it becomes developed or exaggerated sufficiently to become readily outwardly apparent. This was the case in the following two instances of Behavioral Compensation for small stature.

Case 73
Behavioral Compensation for Small Stature

A twenty-four-year-old graduate student was the smallest one in his class. Among his associates he was considered a "real scrapper." His general attitude and demeanor left no doubts about his outer feelings of self confidence. He would enter a classroom with a slight swagger, greeting his classmates positively and somewhat aggressively in a raised voice.

On occasion he might lightly punch, push, or jostle folks about, in a friendly manner, but as though to lay a bit of claim to some kind of physical dominance of the relationship. He was quick to respond to an intellectual challenge, which from his history, proved to be a similar kind of quick response to earlier physical challenges as a boy. At times a statement would be taken as a challenge where none had been intended.

His general attitude in living and the picture he presented were reminiscent of nothing so much as a bantam rooster. Further, he was known for his quick temper, becoming involved in fisticuffs occasionally even after he was in his twenties. His relative aggressiveness, defensiveness, and cockiness were in Compensation for inner and more hidden doubts and fears of inadequacy stemming primarily from his limited physical endowment.

Many examples are present in history and literature of Compensation for physical factors. Napoleon is a striking instance of "power compensation" for short stature. This has been true of other conquerors and rulers—modern and ancient. Among the latter, Alexander was notably small of stature in the light of his conquering and heroic roles. Alexander was ultimately deified and for several centuries was worshipped in Egypt and elsewhere in the Middle East. This will bring us shortly (following the next heading) to another interesting aspect of Compensation in a national kind of application.

The tall woman.—Above-average height can be equally disturbing, particularly for women. Their conscious efforts at Compensation include such direct efforts as wearing flats, special attire, and make up. Less conscious endeavors at Compensation, in addition, may include social and attitudinal changes. In general these are designed to make oneself less conspicuous.

Self-effacement, shyness, and introversion are examples of character defenses or personality traits which can be contributed to in this manner. The converse of these is illustrated in *Cases 73* and *74.*

(2) National Compensation

Sometimes the leaders and/or the general public of a nation by enhancing reputation, emphasizing various positive aspects of the "national character," physical size or prowess, may accomplish or seek to secure a certain amount of Compensation. This can be sought for objectively realistic or subjectively overvalued national deficiencies, lack of historical achievement or progress, for character-tarnishing kinds of exploits, or less heroic stature as to character or physique.

This is an interesting major group type of Compensation encountered through both ancient and recent history, for which we might adopt the term *National Compensation.*

Stories, legends, and sagas may also help to undertake this on behalf of a popular figure. Statues of heroes or leaders frequently exceed life size.

In past decades propaganda campaigns have been deliberately

undertaken in these directions, as we have observed both with recent dictators and some present heads of state.

Emphasis on standards for height and weight, school charts, physical development, and on periodic examinations, especially since the turn of the century, while offering many advantages, have also increased the amount of attention, and often concern, given to the relative growth of a child. Some cases like the foregoing example and many more minor instances, may have received some contribution from this source. The following case is very similar to the previous one.

Case 74

Behavioral Compensation in Business and Social Achievement

A young business man was slightly built and short, in contrast to his large, athletic and husky father. This would seem to be an unfair quirk of nature, but the son had compensated in several ways.

He was quick and active both mentally and physically and had been quite successful in business. Socially he was quite popular, despite his aggressive nature. He was a great talker and commanded attention easily, frequently dominating whatever small group he was in. He was rather affectionately nicknamed "Soapy," for the proverbial soap-box of sidewalk orators.

In earlier years, he had tried unsuccessfully to compete in sports and athletic areas. In college he became a great success as a coxswain for the crew, an activity fitting in well with his compensatory attitudes and behavior. While the major unconscious endeavor in this case was Compensation, there were also elements suggestive of Reaction Formation.

B. IN LOVE MAKING

(1) Socially, intellectually, and through nobility of character

Compensation can take many forms. Sometimes an ill-favored person competes poorly, if at all, in romantic affairs. Sometimes in turn he may develop an increased interest in affairs of the heart, an overactive sexual drive, or become an expert dancer or conversationalist, and so on, compensating for other social handicaps to an extent where he becomes perhaps far more successful.

He may compensate in still other ways such as by developing expertness and securing substitute satisfactions, for example, in

202

various intellectual areas. Cyrano de Bergerac compensated for the handicaps of his huge nose by his nobility of character.

(2) Don Juanism

Considerable interesting speculation may be undertaken as to possible compensatory bases underlying the legendary seductive exploits of Don Juan. The following case illustrates one course of development along these lines.

Case 75
Compensatory Success as a Lover

A thirty-six-year-old man in therapy was ill-favored physically, of slight build and unprepossessing features. He had remained single, despite repeated affairs with many women, which he had pursued in rather a compulsive manner. As a lover, he had been a great success. As one interesting little bit of evidence, in one two-month period, five different women made shirts for him as an evidence of their affection and regard!

During childhood and adolescence, he had begun to suffer psychologically from his small size and relative weakness. He admired the bigger, stronger boys who excelled in athletics. This avenue of achievement was blocked to him. He gradually came to seek Compensation through his considerable successes with women. In this endeavor he invested a considerable percentage of his total energy. This, plus the compulsive nature of his activity conveyed correctly the impression that Compensation was not fully achieved.

In other words, on an unconscious level his very successful Don Juan activities did not completely make up for his physical lacks and the significance of these to him. As a consequence he had been steadily driven in compulsive fashion to increase their scope and "success." The compulsive elements in his Don Juanism stemmed from the incompleteness of the Compensation achieved.

C. FOR DOUBTS ABOUT MASCULINITY

In *Case 75* there were also elements of Compensation for doubts about masculinity. There are many subtle ways in which Compensation can play a role in characterologic development as well as in behavior. Herein, as an example, concerns over one's sexual orientation can lead to intrapsychic compensatory endeavors at reenforcement of what one sees to be one's proper position. This kind of defensive development may take place in reference to doubts about either femininity or masculinity.

In the following illustration, these kinds of doubts proved to have an important foundation in the conditioning effect of parental attitudes during early years.

Case 76
Compensation for Doubts about Masculinity

During the course of therapy a young university professor was noted to be making quite an obvious point of his being masculine. His bearing and posture were the essence of maleness. His hair was cropped very close, he often wore heavy shoes or boots, rough shirts, and his clothes sometimes would be better suited to an outdoor type of life than to a university classroom.

Even his physiognomy had taken on a rugged look. There was enough along these lines to readily arouse one's professional interest and curiosity. There was a definite incongruity evident much of the time between his dress, demeanor, and so on, and his professional work.

In brief, we eventually learned that prior to delivery his mother had very much wanted a girl. Her adjustment to the arrival of a young son had been defective, as reflected in his long hair and girlish bangs as a small boy.

He was kept in effeminate clothes for some years. Any evidence of roughness and boyishness was actively discouraged. His interests in competitiveness and sports were also frowned on.

This patient, however, had come to regard his lack of boyishness as a grave deficiency. His deep need to compensate because of his doubts about masculinity entered into his character development. It played a major role in his preferences for clothes, his bearing, and perhaps even in his physiognomy.

D. IN CHRONIC ILLNESS

There is another variation of this mechanism to be encountered in certain cases of chronic illness. Herein one may find Compensation for the effects of the illness, or Compensation for real or fancied deficits which led to one's vulnerability to the illness. This is illustrated in the following.

Case 77
Compensation in Chronic Illness

A fifty-six-year-old patient was 5 feet, 3 inches in height and weighed 165 pounds. She had weighed this much for many years. People in her social circle and her alumni friends freely commented on her obesity. They had well learned that such comments were quite acceptable to her. More than that, she enjoyed these remarks and felt more flattered by them than annoyed! Comments about being fat pleased her.

Overweight and overeating is often more directly related to seeking relief from anxiety, or as an attempt (at least partially unconsciously) to secure comfort and solace. In this case, however, it proved to be largely a long-term, more tangential type of Compensation and security operation following years of illness with tuberculosis.

She had reached her present height at the age of 14 years, but remained at a weight of 90-93 pounds for some years. She was as "thin as a fence rail" and her girl friends called her "Skinny." Her doctor had described her during these years as "thin, undernourished and rundown," none of which had concerned her very much at that time. When she was 20 years old, her younger sister developed tuberculosis and died in a matter of a few months.

At 21 years of age the patient also developed tuberculosis, was seriously ill, and spent several years in a sanatorium.

She had a serious recurrence at 29 years of age, and at one point was given up to die. Subsequently, she became one of the very first people to undergo radical chest surgery, after which she eventually recovered. Weight was a very major problem during these years of illness, in view of which her later compensatory obesity and her attitudes about it become understandable.

After she became ill her lack of weight to her became synonymous with tuberculosis. Thinness was abhorred. Obesity came to equate health for her; invulnerability to tuberculosis specifically, and to illness generally. As long as she was fat she could remain calm and at ease. Obesity became a successful Compensation for the illness, its effects, and her possible further vulnerability to it.

An interesting sidelight in this case concerns her parallel attitudes toward milk, which of course can offer some added dynamic ramifications of interest. Originally, milk was an anathema to her. From 18 to 21 years of age she drank it occasionally, and only under the pressure of her doctor's insistence. After she was 21 years old, it became a matter of much greater urgency. Ever since she has consumed at least two quarts daily.

For more than 25 years now, however, she has enjoyed it greatly; would not miss it! She "feels better" when she drinks milk, a feeling which is far more psychologic than physical. It makes her feel "safer," "more protected," "comfortable," and "less vulnerable." Milk has become an important *soteria* for her, as to an extent has also her obesity.

E. FOR POOR SCHOLASTIC STANDING

Compensation is a major type of psychologic defense and as such is very widely, if not universally, employed. Many instances of Reaction Formations can be interpreted as subserving a compensatory need. I recall several cases marked by belligerent attitudes which had developed as Reaction Formations, or as Inversions of underlying, more tender feelings. These have compensatory elements (*see Case 53*).

At times we see belligerent or bullying attitudes develop as more clear-cut Compensations for various kinds of real or subjective deficiencies. In the following case, behavioral Compensation was undertaken for poor scholarship. It illustrates the bully, aided by his stature, who endeavors in this way to compensate for his poor intellectual ability.

Case 78
Compensation Attempted through Being a Bully

H. S. had never been able to do well in school. His classroom work was poor, his thinking slow, and his level of interest in academic matters less than normal. His grades seldom reached average. In size and strength, however, he was above average and made sure everyone knew this. He had a chip on his shoulder, acted belligerently and was boastful. He pushed other boys around in school, was quick to hit someone who crossed him, and insulted the girls. He took every advantage of his size, and woe to the classmate who dared to make fun of his lack of scholastic ability!

This boy was compensating for his real inner feelings of inadequacy and inferiority over his miserable classroom showing. Behaving as a bully, he endeavored to bolster his poor level of self-esteem. He secured a measure of attention and recognition of a sort, but the end results as far as acceptance and being liked by his schoolmates were concerned were nil. It was a tragically self-defeating kind of defensive endeavor.

206

F. IN PSYCHOTIC PATIENTS

Those who work in mental hospitals encounter many interesting kinds of Compensation. Some of these develop as a consequence of the deficits of illness. Patients suffering with mental deficiencies of varying degree often gain a reputation for their application to assigned tasks and routine. Various skills and faculties may be developed to compensate for memory defects or other impairments.

(1) Compensatory denials

Some, whose extramural personal relationships had been tragic failures, will occasionally make very good ones with one or more selected individuals within the hospital setting. Patients who have had lobotomies may deny their surgery or resulting deficits, or attempt to compensate for them. There are many and varied instances, of which the following two cases illustrate several of the foregoing points.

Case 79
Compensation for Prior Failures

J. L. was a thirty-eight-year-old patient who had suffered with schizophrenia for nearly 10 years, during most of which time he had been hospitalized. For a considerable period, he had been withdrawn, keeping to himself and avoiding contacts. Gradually it became possible through therapy for this to be somewhat modified and shortly afterwards he was assigned to a gardening detail. Here he applied himself with diligence, even to tasks that were most routine or shunned by others. He took a great deal of pride in his work and would literally beam when he was praised. He made himself so valuable that his supervisors at work were loath to have him leave the hospital on visits (a privilege which he himself did not seek and didn't seem to enjoy). This has continued for some years.

Both overprotected and rejected in his early years, this man had had substantial foundations laid for chronic mental illness. His interpersonal relationships and social adjustments were never adequate. Striking in his case (and important to him personally) had been his total inability to perform adequately in any type of work. His earlier employment history had been very poor. His hospital employment provided his first success in this area and was a most important one for him. His application, his efforts, and some of his satisfaction resulted from Compensation, the operation of which was mainly unconscious.

207

Case 80
The Compensatory Use of Confabulation [3]

John M. was a thirty-six-year-old, married patient who had been admitted some months before to a mental hospital with a diagnosis of Korsakoff's psychosis. This was a consequence of his chronic alcoholism. He suffered from all the typical symptoms of this condition. When asked what he had done on the preceding day, he gave a plausible and coherent account of a shopping trip in town, accompanied by a visit to the home of his sister.

His activities of a week before were likewise described in some detail. These accounts were sequential and related in a convincing manner. Actually, the patient had not left the ward since admission! He was compensating for his symptomatic memory defects by confabulation, the filling in of actual memory gaps by imaginary experiences, which he related as though they were factual. Confabulation is a frequent development in this type of alcoholic psychosis. It served as a Compensation for the deficits of illness in his case, and might also be regarded as a form of Rationalization.

G. AS A CONSCIOUS EFFORT

One may often have to differentiate Compensation as an unconscious mental mechanism from the many instances of compensation which take place through conscious effort. At times this can be a difficult matter. Conscious efforts at Compensation are universal. It may prove impossible to draw a clear-cut distinction between where conscious Compensation leaves off and unconscious Compensation begins.

Men of small stature and adolescent boys frequently work at exercises, sports, gym routines, weight lifting, and so on, in efforts to "build themselves up," to make up for physical deficiencies. These may be realistically evaluated, may have in them too much of the subjectively inaccurate, or may serve as an outward focus for more hidden and deeper neurotic problems.

(1) Cosmetic and athletic

Other areas which provide a frequent target for both conscious and unconscious compensation relate to the changes which transpire in consequence to the aging processes. Many correctively intended cosmetic, and so on, efforts, particularly on the part of women, and athletic ones by men, for instance, are intended as compensatory. Their success may vary, as may their relative transparency to an observer. Occasionally, they may be rather pathetic or even ridiculous.

The following instance was mainly a conscious and effortful compensatory endeavor to maintain an impression of youthful vigor and a competitive position, although there were likely unconscious elements as well. It illustrates in more extreme fashion the position of men who want to appear to be younger, more active, and more virile.

Case 81
Conscious Compensation for Age

J. B. was considerably over the age of his contemporaries as a first lieutenant in the army. He had been recalled to active duty in this rank as a reserve officer, some years after the close of World War II, when he had been discharged as a major.

J. B. was most acutely aware of the differences in chronology, and was far more concerned about ways in which this might handicap him, or weaken his competitive position, as he saw it, in distinction to the possible advantages which some might see to accrue in this situation.

As a consequence he made every effort to compensate for what he considered to be his deficiencies resulting from age and diminished physical vigor. He paid the most minute attention to trifling details of his company's training. He was conspicuous as the first man up each morning, took the foremost position in any athletic event, and went all out to equal or better the physical or military achievements of his compeers.

Most of the results were indeed commendable from the standpoint of the service, and many of them likewise from that of the officer. Occasionally, an incident was pathetic or even ludicrous. One such example took place during barracks inspection when he would leap in the air *à la Tarzan,* chinning himself on a rafter, to look for dust.

(2) Contributions to leadership

Conscious efforts at Compensation can be very successful. They have been employed, with considerable social (as well as personal) benefits to an increasing circle of people. Their employment has also contributed through aiding in the development of a leader. There are a number of historical examples, illustrated by the following:

Case 82
Demosthenes Compensated for a Speech Impediment

Demosthenes, the famous orator and statesman of ancient Greece, suffered in early life from a very serious speech impediment. He became most determined to overcome his handicap. Accordingly, he repeatedly practiced public speaking, frequently while in the hills by himself. History tells us he placed pebbles in his mouth to make enunciation even more difficult.

This was a consciously directed effort to overcome a recognized handicap. Its success was demonstrated by the lasting fame that Demosthenes achieved as an effective public speaker.

Case 83
Theodore Roosevelt's Successful Compensation

Another example, this time from modern history, is that of Theodore Roosevelt, who in early life was a rather slight person, endowed with little physical stamina. At one time he was suspected of being a victim of potential or active tuberculosis. With great personal determination, he decided he would overcome his physical limitations. He headed out West, where he undertook a vigorous physical régimen designed to compensate for his frailties.

As a result of great efforts over a period of time, he gradually developed such great physical stamina that he later was able to lead the famous Rough Riders successfully in the Spanish-American War. This achievement contributed considerably to his later personal renown and political career.

3. DYNAMICS OF COMPENSATION

A. IN RESPONSE TO INNER NEEDS

(1) Acceptance, love, attention, recognition, and self-esteem

Menninger [4] regards Compensation as a mechanism which automatically tries to make up for deficiencies of any sort, whether these be perceptual, physical, social, or whatever. As he views this process, it may be accomplished automatically and unconsciously, and at other times it may also be a conscious and deliberate process. In either case, adjustments are achieved which are more satisfactory than had been secured prior to the employment of the psychologic mechanism.

Compensation may be employed in response to inner needs for acceptance and love. It may represent the unconscious endeavor for recognition, for attention, or for self-esteem.[3] As noted earlier, its employment may be the result of actual inferiorities, deficiencies

210

and loss, or it may follow purely subjective feelings of this nature. I have limited the naming of Compensation as a mental mechanism to instances of its unconscious employment. Compensation may be a very direct and relatively simple process. Through it the individual unconsciously seeks to make up for the loss or deficit.

(2) Alfred Adler and his contributions

The work of Alfred Adler requires comment in our discussion of Compensation. Adler was particularly impressed with the initial position of helplessness of the infant. Thus each individual begins life in a most helpless position *vis à vis* both nature and (powerful) adults about him. As Adler viewed the consequences of this to the developing psyche he saw the defensive results lead to compensatory strivings for power and mastery. One's major goal therefore would become one of seeking superiority in response to— or at the least compensation for—his basic feelings of inferiority. We owe to Adler the widely adopted term (and concept) of inferiority complex. The mental mechanism of Compensation becomes a dynamism of major importance indeed when one fully accepts these bases of Adlerian theory.

With the operation of Compensation more energy is required to keep it operative and effective than with Sublimation. The basic drives do not achieve full and unimpeded discharge as in Sublimation (where the direction of discharge is the major alteration) which we observed in Chapter 3. Accordingly, the satisfactions and the results from Compensation may well be limited and fail to really achieve the sought-after resolutions of conflict and the relief of the initiating needs. Should the failure of the Compensation be too marked, the drive to compensate may become increasingly absorbing, exaggerated, pathologic, lead to the enlistment of other mechanisms, and contribute to emotional illness of various types.

(3) The goal of parental acceptance, approval, and love

We must recognize that this major mental mechanism also can operate in many ways that are far more complex and subtle— considerably more so than in some of the fairly superficial, striking, and usually more obvious instances selected (often with these criteria in mind) as illustrations.

In the following case, the major attempted unconscious endeavor was to secure parental acceptance, approval and love.

Case 84
Compensation in Seeking Acceptance

James W. was the only child of a father who had been a "little All-American" quarterback. He had been sickly from infancy, had never developed well physically, and was unable to keep up in sports and similar activities with his contemporaries among children in the neighborhood. Not infrequently, he bore the brunt of their pranks. Although he was sheltered in many ways by his parents, as a reflection of their impatience, they also tended at times to ridicule him, as did his classmates. In view of his lack of physical prowess and accompanying incoordination, he did very poorly when his father sought to teach him sports. These he could never master. His inexpertness here also had important implications as to (and for) the parent-child relationship.

Before the age of 10 years, however, the boy had mastered a knowledge of sports history, and already knew the rules of all the major sports in some detail. Being raised in a small college town in northeastern Ohio where football was followed closely, his interests in sports were further accentuated. This interest and the development of an allied but substitutive skill in know-how *about* sports represented his Compensation. Its unconscious "intent" was to serve as a means for gaining acceptance or love, originally from his parents.

As a college sophomore, 19 years of age, Jim was short in height, with a round, rather ungainly "roly-poly" type of figure. He was extremely desirous of making friends, particularly with the more athletic members of his fraternity. At times it was as if he would be trying to literally cling to his friends and not let them get away, as for example when he would take hold of a classmate's arm when talking with him. In most instances, his conversation turned to sports, about which he was becoming an authority.

As part of his curriculum, James took courses in radio and broadcasting, and later became the sports announcer on the college radio station. He also became assistant (and later) manager of the football team. In his junior year, he took courses in football and basketball, officiating in the Physical Education Department, and becoming an official for intramural events, with an occasional opportunity to referee varsity scrimmages and junior varsity games. After such occasions, he was very much excited, elated, and was most pleased upon being congratulated.

Jim's compensation continued in the field of sports through his therapy (age 33–35 years), although gradually better understood, and with him eventually controlling it more than it controlled him! Today he is a football and basketball official, sports director for a radio station, and newspaper sports columnist. The basis for his compensatory efforts lay more directly and more readily apparent to the trained observer in his seeking approval, acceptance, and love, than is the case in many instances in which Compensation is a major intrapsychic mechanism. Features in this example point up a close relation to the mechanism of Identification and its similar unconscious aims. By these endeavors, he had achieved a measure of success in securing approval from his parents, parental figures, and associates.

B. TO COUNTERACT FEELINGS OF INFERIORITY

(1) New satisfactions for blocked ones

The origin of Compensation is found by Stevenson and Neal [9] to arise from feelings of inferiority and insecurity. Thus, when an individual regards himself as handicapped, especially in relation to other people, he may employ the mechanism of Compensation to counteract the inner dissatisfaction coming from such feelings of inferiority. Young [11] points out how in our present-day society, the individual has to seek substitutive satisfactions to those of his desires which are personally or socially unacceptable. One way to offset one's own sense of incompetence or inadequacy is through utilizing the defense mechanism of Compensation. In this way one may unconsciously secure satisfactions which would otherwise be prohibited via more direct expressions of one's consciously disowned inner desires.

Young sees Compensation as a method for the reduction of tensions which arise from a sense of defeat or inferiority. A trait other than the one leading to the feelings of inferiority is emphasized in preference, thus providing a measure of defense against the sense of inferiority. In other words, when achievement is lacking, and to reduce the discomfort of thwarted drives in a certain direction, the individual unconsciously employs Compensation. This serves also as a method of directing attention, one's own and that of others, away from the deficiency in question. Thus, bullying may also be a way of asserting physical strength and adequacy for a person who is not strong physically and who is thus considered inadequate. By its use, the person may be able to deceive not only others but also himself as well, with a consequent lessening of inner tension and anxiety. (See Case 78.)

O'Kelly and Muckler [6] regard Compensation as an active attack on frustration, and as basic to most mechanisms. They offer as examples: Abraham Lincoln, definitely "underprivileged" by today's standards, who had to study in the light of the fireplace, walking miles to borrow books so that he could read in this way; the hunchback Steinmetz becoming a dominant figure in electrical engineering, to make up for his unfortunately misshapen frame; Edison with his serious handicap of deafness, inventing the phonograph to bring sounds to the world; Negro leaders compensating for feelings of inferiority in present-day society; the slum lad stealing cars to compensate for his lack of a place in society; and the adolescent girl entering upon a life of sexual aggressiveness as an unconscious Compensation for the lack of love in her family circle.

(2) Lacks and deprivations leading to strivings for power

The puny adolescent, unable to compete favorably with his peers at school in athletic prowess, or in dating girls, is another fairly familiar example, devoting all his energies to studies and intellectual pursuits so that he can excell in these. Shaffer [7] also remarks on the substitution of mental superiority for physical inferiority. (*See Case 74.*) He notes too how the rabid reformer may actually be compensating by means of his excessive opposition to vice, for some of his own forbidden and consciously disowned inner drives.

It is an interesting and a dramatic paradox that by Compensation great and oftentimes excessive strivings for power and prestige spring from inner feelings of inferiority or self-doubts, or weakness of some sort, of which the person may be entirely unaware. [8]

(3) Successes in alternative areas

The younger brother who is unable to successfully compete with achievements of an elder sibling who preceded him in school may compensate by successes in another area. A younger child thrown into an older group may seek to compensate through aggressive attitudes or behavior. A socially inept college student from an underprivileged background made up for his lack of friends by securing sympathy, attention, and advice as a consequence of much publicized and magnified handicaps and crises in his personal and family life. The slightly-built soldier may distinguish himself in training or in combat.

An obese and physically unattractive girl compensated for a lack of dates and individual attention by developing social and entertainment skills that resulted in her being sought after for parties. An amputee may come to excell in various areas as a compensatory development. In such a fashion one extremely successful engineer emerged from being a pre-operative professional failure.

C. CONTRIBUTIONS TO VOCATIONS AND AVOCATIONS

All kinds of vocations and avocations may have important roots in internal compensatory needs. In the following case these needs led to a major interest in automobiles.

Case 85
Compensation in Powerful Motors

A thirty-three-year-old single man had a very shifting and impermanent job history. This was despite his possession of a considerable amount of mechanical ability and ingenuity. He suffered from chronic feelings of inadequacy, and self doubt, and from serious difficulty in working out constructive relationships with others. He felt blocked and frustrated at every turn. In particular he had felt his position in life to be one of overwhelming impotence and powerlessness.

This man's all-absorbing hobby was cars—powerful ones which he rebuilt himself. Through this vitally important activity he had unconsciously sought and secured a significant amount of psychologic compensation. He would mount a particularly powerful motor in an old standard frame and body, adopting or building necessary drive shafts and gears. On one occasion he successfully used a 300-hp. Cadillac engine in a 1948 Dodge; another time an aircraft engine in an old Pontiac. Even more important to his satisfaction than the building was the driving.

"I get a terrific kick from the feeling of power. It makes me feel real good. I like to hear the power of the engine and to feel it go . . . Racing is not important. It's not the speed. It's the feeling of exhilaration I have about the power . . . the response to my wishes . . . my control. . . . Here I'm the one in control! I'm the boss!"

Here the feeling of adequacy in controlling and handling a terrifically powerful engine compensates for his own deep feelings of powerlessness and impotence. A number of other rather interesting factors entered into the satisfactions he derived. For example, the concealed nature of the power was also important. To casual appearance, his cars would seem

215

rather run-down and disreputable, hardly capable of tremendous acceleration and performance.

He also took pride in his skill of handling his disguised behemoths of the highway. He wouldn't expose passengers to such risks, but he delighted in taking curves at top speed, especially dangerous ones. On one curve several people had met death "only doing around 60." He boasted, "I can take cars around that curve at 85 and 90, and I've done it a fair number of times." In this dangerous and unlawful, but personally satisfying way, he "proved" he was the real master of the power, and compensated for his self doubts and inadequacy in so many areas of living. Further, he successfully competed with others (the prior losers) for the highest possible stakes—those of life and death.

4. OVERCOMPENSATION; CHARACTEROLOGIC HYPERTROPHY

A. PROGRESSION BEYOND AN OPTIMAL POINT

(1) Hypertrophy equating pathology

It is generally agreed that Compensation is a nearly universal mechanism which can aid in the maintenance of mental health. Compensatory efforts may and frequently do perform a useful function. In this category belong such conscious efforts as those of Demosthenes and Theodore Roosevelt (*Cases 82* and *83*).

On the other hand, conscious and unconscious compensatory efforts may progress beyond an optimum point, becoming progressively more pathological. At such a point the process may be termed overcompensation. Overcompensation leads to psychologic pathology. Herein one can draw an analogy to what transpires in organic types of disease, in which the end result may be structural hypertrophy of an organ or part. Similarly, in the area of man's emotions, there may be an analogous kind of characterological hypertrophy.

(2) Undercompensation : the schizoid withdrawal

Young [11] holds that overcompensation results when the individual develops excessive and emotionally substitutive habits and attitudes. He also describes "undercompensation", in which the individual, overwhelmed by his own sense of inferiority (whether the inferiority be real or imagined) withdraws from reality and engages in day-dreaming, with consequent danger to any realistic relationship to the environment.

O'Kelly and Muckler [6] compare overcompensation to the hoarding behavior observed in rats starved in infancy. Even though they now obtain all the food necessary for normal health and development, they are seen to hoard food as if they were trying to compensate or make up for the starvation of their early days. Overcompensation may be regarded in a somewhat analogous fashion as a kind of psychologic "hoarding," that is, a storing-up of more compensatory achievement than is actually needed for present purposes.

B. OVERCOMPENSATION HAVING MANY RESULTS

(1) The need for achievement and success

In our complex civilization, the individual finds himself in a social environment where he is subject to much frustration. The rewards bestowed by society today are for those who can show achievement and who can attain what is termed "success." With this emphasis on achievement and success, it is easy to understand how the individual turns to overcompensation, which can give him in his own eyes, and perhaps in those of others as well, the semblance of achievement and success. Overcompensation can also lead to overcompetitiveness.

Menninger [4] writes that overcompensation may be used unconsciously, not so much to fool others "to get away with it," but rather to protect one's sensitiveness, one's own pride, one's ego. Further, an over-meticulous, over-conscientious man, painfully honest in all his dealings, may really be hiding an inner disowned propensity for dishonesty. The latter unconsciously serves to cultivate the excessive habits of honesty which win for him the social esteem which he craves, which are opposite to his inner propensity, and further, which aid in its control. In this description, overcompensation is akin to Reaction Formation.

(2) The promotion of a good self evaluation

Stallworthy [8] refers to the man with the guilty conscience who overwhelms his wife with an unexpected and lavish display of affection and generosity because, consciously or unconsciously, he is making up for, that is, compensating for, unacceptable thoughts or deeds. These are frequently aggressive in nature. Menninger [4] notes that sexual overactivity in men often is an unconscious over-compensation for feminine attributes which they feel they possess, but which they unconsciously feel they must make up for and (thus) hide. (*See also Case 76*, page 204).

Everyone wants to have a good opinion of himself. Everyone wants to be capable of success, to have a sense of achievement. Stevenson and Neal [9] comment that by means of overcompensation the individual is able to persuade himself that he is indeed capable of success. In an effort to equal or to surpass others, in this competitive world of ours, human beings may become selfish, bullying, studious, energetic, pompous, domineering, loving, and so on, through their unconscious overcompensations.

5. ADDITIONAL ASPECTS

A. RELATION TO OTHER DEFENSE MECHANISMS

(1) Rationalization, Identification and Inversion

Compensation is found to operate akin to, or in close association with, other mental mechanisms. Rationalization, or the trying to find "good" reasons or excuses for one's conduct or thoughts or opinions (*see Case 80*) is one of the related ones. *Case 84* illustrates the close relationship which can exist between Compensation and Identification. Compensation may become so close to Reaction Formation or to Inversion that it is difficult to separate them. This is illustrated in the following example:

Case 86
Compensation for Disapproved Behavior

A 35-year-old single storekeeper described himself as having "always been the black sheep of the family." He based this upon intermittent episodes of drinking, sometimes accompanied by aggressive belligerent behavior and a number of arrests.

Except for these episodes, his behavior was regarded by many as most exemplary!—and therefore they were all the more difficult to explain. It was a rather unusual paradox in behavior. He had worked continuously at his one job for 12 years, without ever missing a day's work or taking a vacation. He was "most devoted" to his mother and sisters and the majority of his earnings had gone to their support.

218

He suffered from strong inner convictions of unworthiness and guilt about his lapses. His exemplary conduct otherwise, and his painfully self-sacrificing attitudes toward his family were partly unconscious endeavors at Compensation. In turn, in their being so overdone, these tended to keep the cycle going. In this example, as in the one to follow (*Case 87*), the Compensation may be regarded as being provided through Reaction Formations, illustrating the close relationship possible between these two major mechanisms.

(2) Reaction Formation and Denial

Brierley described Compensation and Reaction Formation as closely allied and differing only in scope. Thus, Compensation (or overcompensation) would become Reaction Formation if the individual's subjective deficiencies are compensated for, by the development of character traits in the opposite direction. These outwardly opposing personality traits that we find in these instances may be thought of as being brought on by the need for Compensation. In such instances, Compensation serves also as a form of Denial of attributes that are more hidden. These have been rejected because, causing tensions and anxiety, they were unacceptable. The following case, reported earlier, is a brief illustration:

Case 87
Compensatory Character Development by a Military Officer

An Army General was actually on the shy, sensitive, passive, introverted, and insecure side underneath. He had "compensated" for these disowned, more basic, and inner attributes by the outward development of those traits associated with the more outward-going, extrovertive, confident, and brave person. In this instance, the person described obscured (that is, obliterated or overcame) his original difficulties by their repression and replacement with the above kind of opposite characteristics. Partly, these needs had led to his seeking a military career in the first place.

These traits he had developed were maintained until tremendous external stresses under war conditions proved too great. He had been a successful military officer who had volunteered for and served well in a number of important combat assignments. Ultimately he suffered an acute emotional breakdown under severe and prolonged battle stress.

219

B. RELATION TO EMOTIONAL ILLNESS

The obsessive patient, as a Compensation for his hidden self-doubts, and out of a strong inner need for acceptance and recognition, may exhibit great pride in his intellectual attainments. This may be an outgrowth similar to the type of instance previously mentioned of the puny, non-athletic youth who puts all his interest and time and energy into intellectual pursuits and achievements, in order to compensate for his weak physique.

In analogous fashion, Compensations may develop for many kinds of subjective or real psychologic deficits. Compensation may be the consequence of handicapping illness; organic or emotional. Patients with paresis, with its tendency to bodily and mental loss of strength, often exhibit delusions of grandeur, almost as if they needed to compensate for the physical and mental decline brought on by the disease. (*See also Case 84*).

The delusion of grandeur may develop so that it finds expression in some of the paranoid expressions to be found in psychotic reactions. There are many other ways in which Compensation can be uncovered as operative in emotional illnesses, as it can be found in many whose level of emotional health is reasonably good.

C. PARENTS, COMPENSATION, AND VICARIOUS SATISFACTION

(1) Use of Rationalization

A special use of the mental mechanism of Compensation is often made, unconsciously, by parents. Frequently, they may in this fashion try to make up by and through their children for what they themselves missed in life. Parents may secure various kinds and degrees of vicarious satisfaction in this way. The thwarted prima donna, or concert pianist, may try to force singing or piano lessons on her daughter, regardless of the child's interest in, or adaptability for, this type of training. There is usually considerable Rationalization in connection with this, the mother assuring herself and others that what she is trying to do is to give the child "every advantage, cultural and otherwise." In reality, she may be trying to compensate for her own earlier lack of success (or opportunity) in this respect.

Likewise, many a non-professional man has tried to push his son into the study of medicine or the law, because in his own youth he may have desired very strongly to become a physician or lawyer, but was prevented by any one of a number of considerations. Often enough in this kind of instance, the parent is totally unaware and unconscious of his own inner drives in this connection; although the child may sense some of the basis, and bitterly resent it! Oberndorf [5] wrote of the mother who is herself still emotionally dependent on her own parents, being not yet fully mature, and who may aim to bind her children to her more closely. Their (the parents) nearness reassures her against her own feeling of weakness as a spouse, and may further act as an overcompensation against her unconscious feelings of hostility against the children.

D. COMPENSATION IN BEHAVIOR

We have seen a number of illustrations in which attributes, character traits, or personality development, and so on, have been influenced through a need for Compensation. At times this also becomes apparent through one's behavior, in which the "making up for" process does not have to be deeply unconscious.

A patient recently reported an instance in which he became angry with another man at work and exploded in an angry outburst and subsequent altercation. He was noted by others correctly as being "extra nice to everyone else the balance of the day." He was endeavoring to make up, that is, to compensate, for his earlier behavior.

6. SUMMARY

Compensation is a major mental mechanism, operating unconsciously, through which one attempts to make up for real or fancied deficiencies. Compensation is sought because of feelings of inferiority to secure ego reenforcement, largely through increased attention, approval, acceptance or love. Conscious efforts at Compensation are likely universal. The unconscious mechanism is widely employed.

Concerns over physical endowment lead to its frequent employment. Examples concerning height and weight were discussed. The concept of *National Compensation* was noted. In the process of enhancing public figures, Compensation may be undertaken on their behalf. Athletic skill and physical development, or scholastic absorption and attainment may result from compensatory efforts. Compensation was discussed in Don Juanism and in relation to doubts about masculinity.

Compensation may follow the deficits of any chronic illness, emotional or physical. Interesting instances are found among hospitalized psychotic patients. The intrapsychic mechanism may be difficult at times to distinguish sharply from conscious efforts in the same direction. Conscious compensation was discussed in relation to the development of special attributes and leadership and in the area of combatting the effects of aging.

Compensation follows inner needs for self-esteem, for recognition, and for acceptance. It can operate in many complex and subtle ways in combatting feelings of insecurity, non-acceptance, and inferiority. Excessive strivings for power and prestige can result. Overcompensation is sometimes employed to describe the exaggerated results of compensatory endeavors which are overdone, that is, progress beyond an optimal point. Some aspects of overcompensation were discussed.

Compensation is related to other mental mechanisms such as Rationalization, Identification, Denial, and Reaction Formation. The characterologic importance of Compensation has been stressed and referred to in a number of examples. In these areas it may be difficult to clearly differentiate from either Inversions or Reaction Formations, one of them operating in the service of the other in the development of character and personality traits. Compensation can play an important role in the healthy personality and also in many cases of emotional illness. It is evident in many areas of family relationships, including parental attitudes. It also is very frequently manifested through its various influences and results on behavior.

REFERENCES

1. COLEMAN, J. C. (1950). *Abnormal Psychology and Modern Life.* Pp. 95, 625. Chicago; Scott, Foresman.
2. LAUGHLIN, H. P. (1959). "The Mental Mechanisms", *Med. Bul., Mont. Co. Med. Soc.* 3(9), 12.
3. — (1956). *The Neuroses in Clinical Practice.* Pp. 77–79. Philadelphia and London; Saunders.
4. MENNINGER, K. A. (1930). *The Human Mind.* Pp. 80, 85–86, 166. New York; Knopf.
5. OBERNDORF, C. P. (1944). "Child-Parent Relationship". In *Psychoanalysis Today.* P. 76. Ed. by Lorand and Sandor. New York; International Universities Press.
6. O'KELLY, L. I. and MUCKLER, F. S. (1955). Introduction to Psychopathology. Pp. 87–91, 608. Englewood Cliffs; Prentice-Hall.
7. SHAFFER, L. F. (1936). *The Psychology of Adjustment. An Objective Approach to Mental Hygiene.* Pp. 159, 161. Boston; Houghton, Mifflin.
8. STALLWORTHY, K. F. (1950). *A Manual of Psychiatry.* Pp. 30–31. New Zealand; Peryer Ltd.
9. STEVENSON, G. H. and NEAL, L. E. (1927). *Personality and Its Deviations.* Pp. 100–101. Springfield; Thomas.
10. THORPE, L. P. and KATZ, B. (1948). *The Psychology of Abnormal Behavior* P. 72. New York; Ronald Press.
11. YOUNG, K. (1952). *Personality and Problems of Adjustment,* Second Edition Pp. 119, 156–157. New York; Appleton-Century-Crofts.

CHAPTER 7

RESTITUTION

. . . amends in response to guilt feelings . . .

1. THE NATURE OF RESTITUTION

A. UNCONSCIOUS AMENDS AND REPARATION

(1) Restitution to relieve inner guilt feelings

Restitution is a major mental mechanism. It is an unconscious intrapsychic process which is employed because of guilt feelings. Through Restitution the ego seeks to make amends to someone who has suffered injury at its hands, to make reparation for real or fancied hurt or wrong doing. It involves the unconscious performance of an act, or actions, designed to make good any loss or damage which is believed to have been inflicted, or hurt which is thought to have been caused. The reparation, if deemed sufficient to adequately indemnify the person, the group, the firm, society, and so forth, serves (or seeks) to relieve inner feelings of guilt and responsibility.

Restitution is one of several mechanisms which are more or less similarly employed in the unconscious endeavor to ease such guilt feelings. One thus seeks to mollify the psychic pain of a disapproving conscience, or superego. The mental mechanisms of Undoing and Unconscious Atonement and Penance also operate toward this goal.

223

(2) Restitution as a useful concept clinically and in teaching

Restitution is one of the more advanced types of mental mechanisms. Less primitive, it belongs with the dynamisms of a so-called higher order. It can only operate in response to the demands of a well-developed conscience; one which can exert sufficient pressure upon the ego for this mechanism to be called into play.

This mechanism, which then we might best formally name *Restitution,* is an ego defense operating outside of conscious awareness whose object is the satisfaction of conscious or unconscious guilt feelings. I have found the delineation, naming, and employment of this concept useful clinically and in teaching.

B. DEFINITION

(1) Restitution to make up for injury or damage

Restitution thus may be defined as *a mental mechanism operating outside of and beyond conscious awareness, through which the ego seeks to make amends and reparation to a person or group for losses which have been inflicted, or for injuries and damages for which responsibility is assumed, as these are subjectively assessed by the perpetrator.*[4] This is an unconscious assessment, which may be quite realistic from an objective basis, partly so, or not at all. Objectivity is not a requirement for the operation of a given dynamism.

Restitution is a defensive intrapsychic process of the ego which is automatically called into play by superego pressure, on the basis of unconscious feelings of guilt and responsibility. Through its operation, the individual seeks to "make up for" his prior bad conduct; for the damage as a consequence to his instinctual impulses, wishes, or fantasies, or from actions in response to them, or for having had them alone.

(2) The distinguishing of Restitution from similar Dynamisms

There is some similarity between Restitution, on the one hand, and Unconscious Atonement and Penance on the other. In Unconscious Atonement, however, the methods of "making up for" the unconscious guilt cover a wider range of methods; Restitution is more specific. Unconscious Atonement may be sought through more diverse channels, which usually include some infliction upon the self of pain, frustration, defeat, injury, loss, or failure. In Restitution, reparation is actually attempted through compensation and reimbursement of the injured party in a rather narrow definite sense, although this, too, is outside of conscious awareness. In Restitution, the connotation of punishment is not implicit to the process, as it is when the mechanism of Unconscious Atonement and Penance is employed.

Undoing is a more primitive and magical process. Through this defense, something which is done is in effect undone. It is then as though the something had never been done in the first place. It is more closely related to direct Repression. It is less specific, less developed, and is likely to be less selective and more massive in its operations. Restitution operates in a more narrow sense and is less frequently encountered. While guilt can also be very important in initiating the dynamism of Undoing, it is not so exclusive, narrow, and precisely limited to this as it is in Restitution. Restitution also involves some restorative act, activity, or behavior. It may at times perhaps be regarded as one way of Undoing. Restitution can also be a means of Compensation. In some Sublimations there can be restitutive elements, and, as we shall see, some restitutive processes approach Sublimation in the resulting constructive activity and social gain.

C. CONSCIOUS RESTITUTION

(1) Many instances representing conscious efforts

Conscious acts of restitution are not uncommon. One does something (or perhaps thinks or feels something) and then upon later reflection perhaps decides that he has been destructive, injurious, or not been fair and seeks to make up for it. As a recent instance, a group of friends sitting together on the beach made one of their number who was knitting, repeatedly lose track in her efforts to count the 118 stitches of the sweater she was starting. Seeing this had "gotten under her skin," one of the friends, a ring leader in the teasing, unobtrusively took over and made the count. As another example, a business man who came to regard a bargain to be too hard on the other party, may modify the terms or make it up to him in other ways. A woman mailed in payment to a store for a small item for which a clerk had failed to charge her. Most apologies (when sincere!) are attempts at Restitution. Others which are not, often seek to convey such an impression.

225

An exacting conscience marked by a most scrupulous kind of honesty may well require considerable effort on the part of the individual to make restitution for a penny or so of too much change. Abraham Lincoln hiked several miles to return a cent or two. Of course, we know that the level of honesty of certain individuals can show glaring inconsistencies; great concern may be shown, and they may lean over backwards about small things, and at the same time quite nonchalantly accept the dishonest benefits of great ones.

(2) An instance of conscious Restitution

In the following interesting small instance, an hourly rate was raised for a tutor. The family concerned talked of this in terms of "fairness," but services had already been received. The new rate of pay was spontaneous, and was made retroactive. Elements of restitution were certainly involved and could not have been far below the surface.

Case 88
A Tutor's Pay is Raised

A family moved to a seashore resort for the summer. Their 15-year-old daughter required tutoring in Latin and the local high school teacher agreed to help. She set her fee at two dollars per hour, after which it was learned that she planned to hold the sessions at the family's cottage, driving six miles each way from her home.

The tutoring began, which she conducted quite conscientiously and well, also frequently putting in extra time. Considering these factors, plus her training, her rate of pay was not commensurate with that of less skilled workmen with far less training and the family began to feel uneasy about it. After several weeks, they raised her pay, quite on their own initiative, making the new rate retroactive to the beginning of her work.

(3) Enforced Restitution

The principle of making restitution for wrongdoing is widely accepted in society. It is implicit to the more enlightened philosophy of criminal law. When a prison sentence has been completed one commonly speaks of the prisoner as having "paid his debt to society." This is a debt incurred by the commission of a criminal act, for which he makes an enforced restitution through serving out his sentence. This may or may not satisfy the individual's *unconscious* sense of guilt; the latter might demand additional restitutive acts, as we shall see in *Case 91*. These may be performed without an awareness of their connection and inner motivation. There are of course other influential aspects in the internal motivating forces which may be present, including those of Atonement, Penance, Compensation, and Punishment.

(4) The prevalence of restitutive acts in human relationships

A worker may feel he has "goofed off" on the job, feel guilty, derelict of his responsibilities, and double his efforts to make up for the lapse. An employer may grant extra time off, or provide some special concession to an employee, as a consequence of feeling he has demanded too much. A mother may buy a child an ice cream cone or take him to a movie because of feeling guilty for a punishment later deemed too harsh. A lover may treat his girl with special consideration and tenderness after an incorrect accusation, an unfair judgment, or shabby treatment. Such efforts are often not designed so much to win favor with the person concerned, perhaps, as to ease his self-critical feelings.

(5) Conscious and unconscious operation

Restitutive acts thus are legion in human relationships and we might recount all manner of instances. The important points here, however, are that they occur with some frequency, and that the line between their conscious and their unconscious operation does not have to be a marked one. The carry-over from one to the other is not very difficult at times, nor too uncommon. Thus, Restitution takes place outside of conscious awareness, in which the intended restitutive act, behavior, or attitude as performed has lost the conscious connection with its inner motivation and goal, which remain unconscious. In other words, the restitutive act may be carried out consciously enough. Its basis is hidden. Explanations which may be made are often enough likely really to constitute Rationalizations. These may be needed to assign a "higher," more acceptable motive for the act. Such an endeavor would thereby aid in maintaining the Repression of the guilt feelings.

227

2. TYPES OF RESTITUTION

A. INTERPERSONAL RESTITUTION

(1) The assessment of responsibility and making amends not within conscious awareness

Making unconscious amends and rendering repayment for real or subjectively assessed wrongs inflicted upon those close to one constitute a major group of the Restitutions which one may encounter. An act or behavior, which may be impulsive and unthinking, or which at the least only leads to guilt and remorse through its subsequent evaluation, is followed by the inner need for Restitution.

(2) Restitution not necessarily major or significant

These Restitutions do not have to be major and significant. They are far more frequently minor. The rarer, more striking instances, however, are likely to attract more attention. These also more usually have to be drawn upon for case examples, in order to better illustrate the point at hand. While this is unfortunate in a sense because of its undue emphasis, it is also necessary.

In keeping with our concepts of mental mechanisms, one is consciously unaware that he has made (or sought to make) Restitution. Such awareness may only be gained through special circumstances or through analytic and investigative therapeutic techniques.

(3) Guilt and restitutive efforts exerting prominent effects

In the example to follow, guilt and its attempted Restitution had played a major role in this young woman's life. This had been true in earlier years, as well as in the present era. Guilt had played a part in her most prominent symptoms, which were those of anxiety. It had entered into her act of seeking therapy. She paid a stiff and undue price for her own satisfactions, in the form of guilt feelings over the partly fancied neglect of her children and impositions on her mother. The continuing battle between her conscience and attempted Restitution exerted a constant influence upon her actions and behavior. Her level of subjectively experienced guilt feelings was quite inappropriate from an objective viewpoint.

Case 89
Neurotically Exaggerated Guilt Feelings Motivate Restitutive Behavior

Sally W. was a young widow with two small children. She had been partially provided for by her husband's insurance and might have made ends meet without working. However, she found a job as a private secretary—a job which she enjoyed very much. Her two small children were cared for by her mother. She might have been thought to be lucky to enjoy her work, but actually she felt quite guilty over this. She also suffered from guilt feelings over her mother having taken over day-time care of the children, something in fact that the mother, a widow herself, actually enjoyed very much—as did the children.

She entered therapy with anxiety symptoms which eventually proved under study to have been precipitated by the attentions paid to her by her employer, who had been courting her and had proposed marriage.

During the course of her therapy, the presence of her strong unconscious guilt feelings in relation to her mother and children were increasingly in evidence through her attempts at Restitution. These were undertaken outside of any awareness of their unconscious intent. Although her mother did not demand it, need it, ask it, expect it, nor even particularly want it, Sally insisted on paying her a sizeable and unrealistically large sum for lodging and board. Her behavior towards her mother reflected an exaggerated concern and solicitude. In addition, she continually showered her children with small gifts and constant attentions to the point where they were very over-indulged.

By her behavior she unwittingly sought to pacify her neurotically severe super ego, which was filling her with guilt feelings over her supposed neglect of her children during the day, and her "impositions" on her mother.

(4) The principle of "Never Enough"

This case illustrated another interesting and fairly oft-seen facet of Restitution; the trend toward its continued and steadily increasing strength and scope of operation. This is what I would propose to call the *"Never Enough"* principle in operation. When this is present and operative, the restitutive activity constantly proves to be insufficient. Also, the behavior, desires, thoughts, and feelings which may lead to its need, neurotically evaluated or not, do not abate, or to the contrary perhaps increase. The Restitutive efforts in turn also increase, but since the underlying conflicts are not resolved, they are never quite sufficient to accomplish their purpose, that is, to indemnify to the extent necessary to fully allay or nullify the unconscious guilt feelings. So it had been with this girl. Guilt-ridden for years, she had formed an unending pattern in which guilt feelings were steadily generated, to be followed as regularly by restitutive efforts. It was only possible for her to surrender this pattern after the unconscious was made conscious. Recognition and acceptance were followed by more objective views, a sounder self evaluation, conflict resolution, and more constructive ways of coping with potential sources of guilt.

Restitution can be sought or can take place in nearly any kind of relationship. It may be observed in parent-child relations, in the direction of the foregoing case, or reversed. It is seen with siblings and in other blood relationships. It can operate in friendships, teacher-student relations, employer-employee, military and business relationships, as well as others. Examples to follow will illustrate several of these.

(5) Restitution leading to a change in attitude

The following instance, drawn from a psychiatric training center, illustrates Restitution following an overly severe "dressing down" given a resident physician in a teaching situation. It is perhaps of interest that while the professor's critical reaction was exaggerated in its severity, his restitutive efforts in turn were also exaggerated. They were remarked upon by the resident group sufficiently to form the basis of several discussions and some continued speculation. None thought the professor was consciously aware of the real basis of his considerably modified attitude and behavior which was exhibited toward the victim of his temper, subsequent to the outburst.

Case 90
A Change of Attitude Seeks to Make Up for a Severe Dressing Down

A leading psychiatrist was especially noted for his warmth, friendliness, and kindliness. He was liked by all. One day he was conducting a meeting of the senior resident psychiatrists as was his wont. Part of the time was devoted to a case presentation. The presenting resident was doing a mediocre job.

After he had offered several rather dubious formulations in sequence the professor lost his temper. In a rather embarrassing scene for those present, he chastised the young resident quite bitterly. It was a reaction which was out of character for the professor and also very much out of keeping with the level of provocation.

After the conference, the chief evidently felt somewhat upset, and apologized to the resident. During the next few months, his attitude toward this particular resident underwent a complete metamorphosis. Previously, he had been a bit skeptical about this man's potential and cool toward him in comparison to others. Following this incident, he went out of his way to be considerate and friendly. He very shortly volunteered to write a letter of recommendation for the resident, and did several other things for him which were "beyond the call of duty." Gradually the resident came to have a favored position in his group, in some contrast to his relative position during the two preceding years. The situation gave all of the appearances of attempted Restitution by the professor to make up for his guilt feelings over his earlier attack upon the young doctor (plus perhaps his prior feelings, and unconscious factors including Identification with an earlier figure).

The other residents as a group felt that (a) the attempted Restitution was exaggerated, (b) that it reflected thereby an undue amount of unconscious guilt, (c) that the professor was consciously unaware of the real reasons for his modified attitudes (he remarked several times as to how much better a student the resident had become, how he was more perceptive; observations not agreed with by his compeers), and (d) that these restitutive endeavors had really "paid off" for the resident, that is, being jumped upon and embarrassed had indeed been a lucky break!

B. PUBLIC RESTITUTION

(1) Voluntary restitution by the individual

This type of Restitution, which I would propose to term *Public Restitution,* includes (a) that which is demanded and required by the public from an individual through the process of law, and (b) that which is voluntarily made to the public by the individual.

Each year various municipal, state, and federal agencies receive unexpected remittances from people seeking to make up for past deficiencies. Quite prominent among these agencies is the

Internal Revenue Service. However, many bureaus and departments receive them. So also do many banks and business firms. Occasionally, one of these is sufficiently interesting or unusual to be picked up in the press. Far more of them are not noteworthy enough for this however, and receive routine treatment, and no public notice. Most of these are deliberate and planned. The persons involved may identify themselves or prefer to remain anonymous. Many of the sums involved are petty, but occasionally sizeable amounts are sent in. The overall total sums involved annually, however, are appreciable.

Not all of the Public Restitutions are so clearly planned however. Also, not all of them are monetary, as Restitutive endeavors can find many and devious pathways. For example, the U. S. Treasury has special accounts made up of unidentified, "lost," and unclaimed funds. These arrive by various routes. However, it is probably safe to assume that a certain proportion of these "losses," "accidents," or failures to be more specific about identity or the purposes of a payment, and soon, are unconsciously motivated in part at least by restitutive needs. Carelessness is by no means necessarily a matter of chance alone. Too often the intensive study of specific instances has demonstrated that it, like other behavioral phenomena, follows the law of scientific determination.

(2) Restitution in criminal cases

Reference has earlier been made to the concept in which Restitution to the public is considered to be completed when a prison term has been served out. The debt has supposedly been paid for that offense and the slate is clean. This may be correct so far as the law is technically concerned. It may not be correct so far as a victim is concerned, nor so far as the individual transgressor or his unconscious is concerned.

The following illustrates how a troubled conscience can lead to continued efforts to make Restitution. These were both conscious and unconscious. As in many instances of Restitution, the conscious acts were the more direct and apparent. Unconscious changes in behavior and character are likely to be more subtle and less apparent, but hardly less significant. They are more likely also be more indirect, being expressed toward others or toward the public generally. In the latter instance, the public or society may be the beneficiary of certain character changes, and Public Restitution can merge into Social Restitution.

Case 91
Public Restitution; Beyond the Technical Payment of One's "Debt to Society"

A young bank clerk was slain in an attempted holdup in the early '30s, leaving a widow and two small children. Two men were shortly apprehended, tried and convicted, and sent to prison for long terms. Nearly twenty-five years later, the widow began receiving small sums anonymously by mail. These became regular and more substantial. Although they continued for years, she never learned (although she may have come to suspect) the identity of the donor, about whom, and whose restitutive needs, I learned in other ways.

One of the men in the robbery had consciously sought in this way to try to make up for the victim's death. Having served more than twenty-two years in prison, where his conduct had been exemplary prior to his parole, he still had not begun adequately to make amends from the standpoint of his own feelings. He had felt a personal kind of responsibility quite beyond any "debt to society," which he had certainly repaid from the technical, legal, and sociologic standpoints. It is also of considerable interest as well that he was not the actual murderer! Guilty he had been, yes. Murder, or even its contemplation, was something else again for him. Here, his was guilt and responsibility by association. He was horrified, revolted, and shaken to the core by this unanticipated development. This had caused him far more trouble and pain than it had the perpetrator. The latter's outward attitude at least had been to scoff and to scorn at any such "softness" as the regrets or feelings of remorse which were voiced by his associate. One might speculate as to whether these were as completely unmixed as maintained, or even whether some of his more hidden needs also exerted pressure for Restitution. In any event, there was little question about the influence of Restitution in the life of the first man.

The payments to the widow were the smaller part. He had developed an apologetic approach to life in general, in which thoughts of the other person's needs or wishes invariably came first. Restitution had placed a stamp upon his character. It was as though he wanted to make up to the public, to make Restitution to the world at large for "his offense." While some seeds of this had been present in earlier years, its real development took place during his early prison years, after his participation in the crime at the age of twenty years.

(3) Prisoners volunteering for experiments

Certain cases of prisoner volunteers for participation in experiments and medical research have in them various elements of Restitution, as well as other mechanisms (that is, Compensation, Undoing, and Unconscious Atonement and Penance). Such work, where there is risk involved for the participants, relies on volunteers. In almost any large prison there are usually quite a sufficient number of such persons, almost regardless of the nature of the experimental work.

(4) The modification of public attitudes toward enforced
Restitution

The demands of the public for Restitution in various offenses were more severe in past decades. More general acceptance of the concept of repayment in full through payment of a fine or serving out a sentence is reasonably new and enlightened. Public floggings and stocks provided a considerable measure of loss of face and prestige, plus a great deal of public embarrassment, shame, and ridicule.

The ancient Talion Law provided an "eye for an eye" and a "tooth for a tooth." In a few areas still, the hand that steals is cut off. Primitive and isolated groups still employ what are, to us, strange and sometimes quite savage methods of meting out punishment, and of enforcing some semblance of Public Restitution which may be quite severe.

C. SOCIAL RESTITUTION

Social Restitution I have so named because society, or some segment of it, benefits from the indirect, less specific, and generalized endeavors at reparation which are employed. The recipients may be, or may have some relation to or association with the originally injured persons or things, little apparent relationship, or none at all. In any event, society in general is a beneficiary.

Repression of the unconscious guilt feelings is maintained through the unwitting efforts at Restitution. The success of this endeavor is somewhat dependent in turn upon the relative success of the restitutive efforts in meeting the needs for them, and the resulting pressures exerted by the superego. This type of Restitution can come close at times in its operation and results to those of the mechanism of Sublimation.

The following example illustrates the operation of this type of Restitution.

(1) Social Restitution: a beneficial consequence

Case 92
Social Restitution Through Charity

A 34-year-old woman entered therapy because of problems in her interpersonal relationships. She was in many ways a very capable and efficient person, serving as Executive Secretary for a large and active humane society, and running its busy animal shelter. However, there was a certain uneasy and forced character to her work, and she was not a very contented or happy person. One would have had no idea, however, that her many services on behalf of her charges had some major roots in unconscious and continuing efforts at Restitution. These stemmed originally from several major incidents in her childhood. She had been the ringleader in the torment and torture of a cat and two dogs. A great deal had been made of these incidents at the time, so much so that she felt exceedingly evil and worthless, and any recollection was most traumatic.

Memories for the incidents had been completely repressed from conscious awareness. This was not surprising in view of the tremendous amount of shame and guilt which proved to be associated. The incidents of torture took place at a time in her development when she was particularly prone to exaggeration of feelings of conscience anyway, and there were also other circumstances which enhanced this. Further, such behavior became increasingly out of keeping with her conscious self picture which subsequently developed in defensive fashion through the years. The defense of this in turn was important, both in the endeavor at Restitution and in reenforcing the earlier Repressions. As time and this process had proceeded, recollections and recognition of her repressed self-evaluation had become increasingly difficult.

Following the clarification of some of all this through her therapeutic work, the neurotic need for continued Restitution gradually dissolved. She did not change her work or interests. In healthy fashion, she became less grim and determined in her attitudes and efforts at work. Because of this and other important insights, she gradually became more light-hearted, human, and friendlier in all her relationships. Life became fuller and more satisfying.

The above is a major and striking example. Efforts at Restitution rarely so permeate character and occupation. However, there are many instances in which Restitution exerts influences in less dramatic fashion. These often include the contribution of various kindly services, charitable assistance and sponsorship to worthwhile and beneficial organizations, civic groups, religious bodies, and social agencies. Social Restitution often unwittingly helps to account for much that is socially useful and worthwhile.

(2) The "Never Enough" principle

Here again, what I have liked to call the principle of "Never Enough" can operate. It is an interesting but also tragic kind of circular reaction in which whatever dynamism, symptom, or other psychic defensive endeavor is called into play, it is *never enough,* as more need is continually generated. Where these kinds of avenues for the disguised expression of inner restitutive needs are utilized, there are some "built-in" pitfalls which can operate so as to keep recharging the needs, for those who are vulnerable. As other examples, some satisfactions may accrue from the prestige, the increased regard of one's friends, public notice or acclaim, and so forth, or one may gain through such mundane ways as tax exemption.

Efforts at Restitution may need to be increased or redoubled as a result of feeling guilt about such internal (emotional) or external gains. Where these were also an important part of the original motivation, this kind of resulting "built-in" guilt may be more accentuated. The guilty feelings in this fashion can tend to grow right along with the efforts at Restitution. The endeavor at Restitution which is made is "never enough."

(3) A church benefits from Social Restitution

The following instance illustrates the influence of Restitution in contributions of work and money to a church. This activity on behalf of a prominent builder and leader of the congregation helped keep in check certain guilt feelings over his more selfish gains from the affiliation, and certain hypocritical factors in his having sought membership in the first place.

Case 93
Social Restitution; Church Contributions to Assuage Guilt over Hypocrisy and Selfish Gain

R. L. was a 58-year-old successful builder in a city of about 50,000 population. He was a leading member of a large local church. For years he had made liberal and gradually increasing donations to the church and its activities. Three years earlier, he had been the originator of a movement to build a

236

new church, had worked very hard toward its realization, and had also made a sizeable contribution to the building fund.

The builder became ill, seriously so. During the course of this illness, his minister made several calls, during which the sick man related to the minister an account of his deep feelings of guilt. He stated that when he originally joined the church it was partly for business reasons. He had been aware of the number of good business contacts he might make, and the financial value of his church affiliation was among the reasons for his seeking membership. He now felt very guilty about this.

He had some partial awareness perhaps that his increasing contributions of interest, time, and money were part of an effort to make up for his having used his church affiliation in this way. However, any full awareness of the restitutive aspects present in his church work was lacking.

His concern was with his guilt, which was as though it were consciously first recognized at this time. He could not appreciate his many useful contributions. These had lost their ability insofar as keeping his guilt feelings repressed, partly under the added stress of his illness, plus some family problems. Fortunately, the minister had an excellent understanding of the situation and recognized neurotic factors in his parishioner's feelings. The alleged hypocrisy in his joining the church was also overstated.

During a series of psychotherapeutic interviews, among other insights, he gained a clearer view of the restitutive factors in his church activities, but at the same time he came to see also their social usefulness and to properly credit himself. Similarly to the patient in *Case 92*, his work in this field did not cease, although he temporarily discontinued all of it for a time, while he was getting his bearings. When it was resumed, it was on a more genuine and sounder basis, and has continued. His church in which he was a leader exercised a powerful and useful influence in his city and made many useful social contributions to the community. His inner guilt feelings and resulting efforts at Restitution had helped substantially in making possible these social benefits. This was an example of Social Restitution.

(4) Social restitution via charity and gifts

When one is aware of its possible operation and perhaps looks for it, the mechanism of Restitution crops up a fair number of times; not infrequently in the work of character analysis with patients. In Restitution guilt is assuaged (or sought to be so) by doing something about it. The following two briefly cited instances are illustrative.

Case 94
Social Restitution Through Charity

A wealthy young woman had had many advantages. These included a wonderful home life, many material benefits, excellent educational facilities, and considerable opportunity to travel. During the course of an analysis, vague guilt feelings were uncovered about having had so much in her life.

She had long felt rather compelled to give away a considerable percentage of her rather substantial income to various charitable causes. This proved to have been a conscience-salving operation. It was an unconscious endeavor at a social kind of Restitution for having enjoyed the many economic and social kinds of advantages which were available to her; for her especially favored position in life.

Case 95
Restitution Through Multiple Gift Giving

A middle-aged woman of some social prominence had entered treatment following a suicidal attempt. What amounted to a social kind of trademark was her largesse as a giver of gifts. Each house guest—and she had many—received an "arrival gift," and on departing a "departure gift." Anniversaries, birthdays, special occasions, and so on for a host of people were marked by gifts. Christmas meant literally hundreds of gifts and ten weeks of intensive, nearly full time, preparation.

During treatment, the early superficial layer of interpretation was that all this concentration upon gift giving was for her a "social promotion" type of activity. The next layer of meaning was that it represented a pathetic kind of buying of attention, friendship, and regard, by a woman really quite insecure, despite her many advantages. Eventually, a third and deeper layer of related meaning emerged, revealing it to be unconsciously sought Restitution. This was mainly in two areas: first (in similar vein to the patient in *Case 94*) as an apologetic and restitutive making up to her acquaintances and friends for the many advantages she had enjoyed in life, and, secondly, as a general kind of reparation and Restitution for the kind of person she considered herself to be, the reflection of an unrealistically low level of self esteem.

D. RESTITUTION BY PROXY

An interesting aspect of guilt feelings is that they do not necessarily have to be confined to acts of one's own. For various reasons, and to various degrees, one may come to feel responsible for an act or for behavior of another. We saw this principle illustrated to some extent in *Case 91*. A parent may feel guilty about the misdeeds of a son, a child about a parent, one sibling about another, or a man about his spouse, and so forth.

This brings us to an interesting type of restitution activity which I call *Restitution by Proxy*. In it one makes Restitution for the performance (or a failure to perform) by another person, and about which he feels in some measure responsible. Illustrations are to be found during psychiatric treatment, although its operation also may be surmised correctly at times in social situations. Validation of these, however, is difficult without considerable ob servation and study. It is illustrated in the following case, in which there were also aspects of resulting social gain.

Case 96
Restitution by Proxy

A young businessman was noted for his participation in civic affairs. He was active in the Lions' Club and headed up its Little League baseball program, into which he put several hours daily each May through September. In addition, he was a leader in a summer camp program for underprivileged children, an officer in the Heart Association, Board member of the Mental Health Association, helped with the local Community Chest, and so on, and could be counted on to actively support and work for any civic project which came along.

People rightly wondered how he managed to keep his business going, and had noted a contrast between his great activity and his father's total lack of interest. Actually, the business had received second consideration many times. The contrast with his father's history of civic inactivity was marked. His father had consistently refused to have anything to do with civic affairs. In view of his father's long-standing prominence business-wise and in other ways, this had been rather striking and had led to various reproaches and critical remarks in the community. The boy had felt this keenly and had made some efforts in turn to interest his father from time to time, which had been brusquely pushed aside. He had learned about civic responsibilities in school, through scout work, and at church school and had been quite impressed.

More than other family members, he had early begun to feel ashamed and guilty over what he regarded as his father's dereliction. As he grew older, the civic activities had seemed to be natural and spontaneous developments. Outwardly, he

239

made light of any favorable notice of his undertakings for the community. Inwardly, he took considerable pride and "felt better." His civic activity was in large measure motivated by the desire to make up for his father's deficiencies in this same area. It was Restitution performed for another, a kind of Restitution by proxy, in which the older man also apparently derived some satisfaction and, although still unable or unwilling to undertake such activities himself, gave some measure of sanction and approval to those of his son.

E. RESTITUTION IN DREAMS

(1) Restitution in day-dreams and fantasy

Restitutive and reparative acts are not confined to conscious efforts nor to outward activity in response to unconscious demands. Restitution can provide a theme for daydreams and fantasy. One may dream of making Restitution. The content of dreams may also reflect otherwise hidden guilt feelings and unconscious wishes for Restitution. At times these are similar to a like expression of Undoing, which may similarly be the subject of dreams.

The next illustration is an example of such Restitution in dreams. It also illustrates another point, in that when the opportunity no longer exists for any direct reparation to the person concerned, its only possible expression may be through a fantasy or dream. This is also an example of what I would call the "dream of regret," which follows the meaning of the poetic lines: *

> ". . . of all sad words of tongue or pen,
> the saddest are these, 'it might have been!' . . ."

(2) Restitution as the manifest theme, the latent basis or the disguised theme in a dream

The surface or manifest content of the dream may or may not reveal this, which can require considerable study and analysis. This was true in the following instance.

---

* John Greenleaf Whittier, "Maud Muller," 1854.

240

Case 97
Restitution in Dreams; The "Dream of Regret"

An older housewife, in therapy, had had a dream which had recurred several times. In it her mother came to visit and she gave her a warm welcome. This was described as a "nice" and "pleasant" dream and the patient was quite content to skip any attempt at its further analysis. With its repetition, however, she was persuaded that it might have further significance. Indeed it did. Briefly, the main points were as follows:

Her mother had died some ten years earlier of a sudden heart attack while living with a sister. The patient had never gotten along well with her, and although she had declared this to be of no moment to her, had secretly wished matters were different. Following her father's death, her mother was without means and had lived with her children, dividing her time among them. The patient had looked forward to her turns unhappily. Further, as it turned out, she had made up some flimsy excuses at the time of her last "turn," so that her mother was living at the sister's home instead, where her sudden death had occurred.

This patient had long repressed feelings of guilt and remorse about her relationship with her mother, antedating her death. The latter episode had greatly reenforced these feelings and had served also as a kind of culmination. She also had some hidden and unrealistic feelings about responsibility for the death in view of her neglect at the time. There had been some "leaning over backwards" noted before in her relations with the sister which had previously lacked explanation. This came to be understood in its more proper light as restitutive in intent.

The dream was one of Restitution. In it she made up for her prior avoidance of the visit and her lack of welcoming by recreating the scene so that it became as she unconsciously wished.

Her feelings of guilt were to this extent assuaged. This was why it was a pleasant and comforting dream. This was also why she wanted to avoid its further study.* Her attitude said in effect: "This is a nice defense. It helps me keep all this painful material repressed. Let's let it alone. Let's not risk making it conscious. Let's not rock the boat!" At the same time the dream helpfully pointed out the existence of the

---

* An interesting instance of the principle of the *Secondary Defense* in operation (*see* earlier references, pages 15–16, 178, and 190–191).

unconscious material and ultimately resulted in bringing about the healthful dissolution of the unrealistic aspects of her feelings through therapy. Its analysis was an important step in her treatment and in her emotional health. It resulted in her gaining new insights, a clearer self-picture, and an escape from some of her unconscious pressures.

F. RESTITUTION IN BUSINESS

(1) Restitution in business by a wide range of means and through referral

In thinking of Restitution, the tendency may be to think in terms of money and finances. Although from our foregoing discussion we have seen that actually this mechanism encompasses a far wider range of activities, still it is often prominent enough in business relationships. As such, it may be conscious, unconscious, or some of both.

The following briefly illustrates one of the many ways in which Restitution can influence business conduct or practices. I suspect it was both partly conscious and unconscious in its operation. It was certainly not deeply submerged in any event.

Case 98
Restitution in Business; by Referral

A business man in a therapeutic session reported casually his practice of referring his customers to a certain firm for services. This represented a minor change in policy and seemed to be worth further inquiry. It proved to be restitutive in design. He had been billed for some work and had believed this to be an under-charge. He did not inquire, but paid the bill as rendered, denying, or at least attempting to deny, that he felt any sense of guilt or responsibility.

Nonetheless, the guilt was there, as evidenced by his need to make a kind of attempted Restitution via the referral of business. Presumably, the profit accruing to the firm through the referred customer, whom they would otherwise not have secured, would make up several times for the amount of his under-charge.

(2) Embezzled funds; Restitution in Abeyance

When funds or goods have been embezzled or misappropriated by an official or employee, efforts at Restitution may or may not occur. They may be conscious or not, but in either event can take odd and varied forms. Many bits of dishonesty are rationalized in various ways. Many remain undiscovered as do any endeavors at Restitution.

In the following instance, we observe conflict between accepting a dishonest gain versus its restoration. This led to an interesting compromise, in which both the gain and its restitution were held in abeyance. This is an instance of *Restitution in Abeyance.*

Case 99
Restitution in Abeyance

A 54-year-old vice president of a large merchandising firm was in intensive psychotherapy because of certain character traits which had resulted in some professional limitations and social handicap. Some years earlier, in the course of his ambitious and energetic career, he had become the manager of a local store for a national chain. While in this position, he had intermittently taken money from the firm. This he had sought to justify to himself on the basis that he was not being adequately paid for the services he performed.

Having moved on in the meantime to another position, after about two years he again worked for them briefly on a temporary basis, during his three-week annual vacation period. Instead of collecting pay for this work, he asked the firm to leave the money due him "on credit against future purchases." After this had been accomplished, he felt more comfortable, although he would still have denied blame or guilt. Note, however, that he did not fully surrender claim to the money when it would have been possible to simply have placed it in with company funds. Both realization of his improper gain, and its Restitution were held in abeyance in a kind of uneasy compromise of his conflicting feelings.

Some period of time elapsed, after which he made some substantial purchases from this firm. Instead of calling attention to the existing credit, he paid the bill in full. In this way, so long as this money remained in their hands, he had made Restitution for the funds earlier misappropriated. However, the money also remained available to him since it was held to his credit and at his call. He had felt very guilty about the money, although he had largely denied this consciously. Actually, through the resulting conflict and the struggle with his conscience, he had paid rather dearly for his early lapses as an Unconscious Atonement.

After his elucidation of this conflict, this man decided to make the Restitution more realistic. How could he do so without confession, in that he was unwilling to have his defection known? Ultimately, he met this dilemma by using the deposited funds to pay for merchandise and mailed a cashier's check anonymously to the firm.

(3) Restitution for poor performance

Although consciously denied, unfairness in business practices, or in the treatment of a client or his property, can result in unconscious guilt. This can produce unwitting efforts at Restitution. In the following instance, such appeared to have been the case.

Case 100
Restitution in Business by Lapses in Billing

In a group of friends at a seashore resort, Tom S. mentioned that he found occasional items missing from his monthly bills at a local boatyard and once he had received no bill at all. This was quite contrary to the experience of the group and of others whom they knew. In fact, the boatyard owner's general reputation was of great exactitude. The contrast was therefore strange.

It seemed that Tom's boat had been stored there the preceding winter, at standard rates. It had not received the customary and expected care, however, but had been allowed to sit out, suffering considerably from the weather. The boatyard man offered various justifications for this and had outwardly accepted no responsibility whatsoever. It seemed quite possible that his lax accounting and billing to Tom, which was so distinctly out of keeping with his usual self, may have reflected less conscious feelings of liability and have represented unwitting endeavors at Restitution.

G. RESTITUTION IN WILLS

(1) Failure of anticipated repayment

Restitution is reflected in occasional wills. This may be conscious or a reflection of more unconscious needs. At times it does not work out as intended. We find this illustrated in the following instance, in which the plans for reparation for anticipated inconveniences misfired.

244

Case 101
Intended Restitution by Will

Following the death of her husband, Aunt Geraldine planned to make her home with a niece. This was acceptable, even though somewhat of an imposition, and so she moved lock, stock, and barrel into the niece's home.

Anticipating that she would have to live with someone, she had earlier made out her will so that a bequest of ten thousand dollars would go to the person "in whose home" she died. This would go toward making up for whatever trouble and inconvenience had resulted. Two years later, while on a week-end visit to the home of a nephew in Boston, she died quite suddenly, and the bequest went to the one relative whom she hardly knew.

(2) Restitution for the means of success

People may feel guilty about the vehicle which led to their success, or to some of its effects. This may have entered into the establishment of several noteworthy memorial trust funds and foundations. This possibility is perhaps notably illustrated by the Nobel awards.

Case 102
Restitution by Will; The Nobel Awards

Alfred Nobel was the inventor of dynamite and several important derivatives. He was also successful in the development and exploitation of his products, and as a business man accumulated a great fortune. Biographical material, including a recent series [5] points up some of his personality problems and emotional conflicts. He was a very lonely and unhappy man, plagued by hesitancy, self-doubt, and probably by guilt.

His new super explosives were vastly superior to those which were hitherto available. While they found all kinds of peaceful uses, they also made possible a new kind of military performance as well—a more destructive kind of war. Through their availability, many more soldiers have died and much more destruction has resulted. Within himself, Nobel must have suffered acutely from the havoc resulting from the martial employment of his explosives.

In his later life, he became interested in movements for peace. Upon his death in the year 1896, a major portion of his fortune was set aside to establish annual awards, of which the more famous are the Nobel Peace Prizes. By devoting funds derived from the manufacture and sale of explosives to promoting peace, a measure of Restitution was sought for their destructive consequences.

(3) Social Restitution related to a condemnatory self evaluation

Mention has been made of the discrepancy between the objective evaluation and the subjective evaluation of one's life, and possible guilt therefrom. Thus, in Restitution, the individual does something else to negate the effects of the original act or conduct, as he "sees" it. Restitution is intended to resolve conflict and to prevent anxiety by its conscience-salving effect. The following instance which I have earlier reported [4] illustrates this kind of Restitution, in which the self picture was certainly not kindly and probably quite inaccurate. In other words, the guilt was very likely of a neurotic level. The scientific foundation which was established was a consequence of an individual's efforts at reparation. It was also highly useful, qualifying this instance also as one of Social Restitution.

Case 103
Restitution by a Successful Industrialist

Some years ago a highly successful "giant of industry" established a benevolent foundation for very worthy scientific purposes. He endowed it financially while living, and still further by his will with a generous portion of the funds and property he had amassed. He had maintained publicly that the basis for this was his interest in helping humanity generally, plus his special interest in a phase of scientific work. In view of his interest in this particular branch of science, there was some considerable truth to this. But his outward explanation did not give the whole picture.

Before his death, while semi-comatose, he "confessed" his deep feelings of guilt about his degree of success and wealth. Setting up the foundation to benefit people was an attempted reparation for his guilty feelings.

Actually by reputation, he was renowned for his high ethics and his strong sense of fair play in his business operations. There had never been any blemish on his record, and his honesty and integrity had never been impugned. He was widely known for his generosity, kindliness, and understanding nature. Note again that the presence and the degree of unconscious guilt does not necessarily show any correlation with reality. The unconscious basis for Restitution is emotional, and its occurrence is an emotional defensive reaction, and not a rational process.

3. DYNAMICS OF RESTITUTION

A. GUILT FEELINGS THE DYNAMIC BASIS OF RESTITUTION

(1) Restitution to satisfy a strict superego

Restitution is a commonly employed and quite conscious process of attempted reparation. It can also operate unconsciously, as a "making up for" process in response to unconscious feelings of guilt. It is closely related to Undoing and to Unconscious Atonement. In essence, it is an internal defensive process.

We can see from the foregoing instances, and from many other less striking examples, how Restitution operates. In many personal ways, and occasionally in larger social areas, Restitution can assist in creative drives. Along these lines Noyes [6] wrote: "The mechanism of relieving the mind of a load of guilt by restitutive acts (a making good or reparation) is not uncommon. Restitution arising from feelings of guilt may become the main motive of life, as exemplified by the indefatigably, almost wearisomely, benevolent person. Operating to a less extreme degree and in a less obvious manner, the restitutive reaction to unconscious guilt may play a large part in a drive toward creativeness." As a part of a more technical discussion, Klein [3] wrote of the sadistic attacks upon the "good" object by the ego and of the attempted "restitution for all the sadistic attacks." Her work which includes this statement was based upon the study of childhood fantasies confided in therapy.

Feelings of guilt arise from a strict superego or conscience. Restitution is an attempt to satisfy such a strict superego, and to assuage or relieve the guilt feelings. We must bear in mind that the demands of the conscience are not necessarily related to realistic standards. All too often its degree of censure is unrealistic, not connected with the actuality existing outside the individual involved, but arising from an individual's inner fears, needs, instincts, and drives. We have seen this illustrated in several of the preceding examples. Thus, a person's unconscious guilt need bear no logical relation to the actual thoughts he has formulated; opinions he has expressed; behavior he has carried out. The unconscious evaluation of the importance of the guilt is highly subjective,

247

and accordingly highly variable. The "badness" of which the person feels himself guilty may be nonexistent; it may be exaggerated and neurotic, or it may be realistic, or a combination of both. From the standpoint of emotional and mental health, recognition of the relative degree of realism of the subjective assessment and the judgment of his guilt by the person involved is of the utmost importance.

(2) Restitution beginning in infancy

In Restitution, something is done in an unconscious attempt to make up for the effects of the original act or conduct; to make reparation for any harm or damage inflicted. Melanie Klein [2] has observed that ". . . the tendency to make Reparation is . . . linked with feelings of guilt." She believes that this process begins in the very early life of the individual, and continues: "When the infant feels that his destructive impulses and fantasies are directed against the complete person of his loved object, guilt arises, and together with it [there arises] the over-riding urge to repair, preserve, or revive the loved injured object." Brierley [1] writes that (according to Klein) ". . . depressive anxieties may also initiate restitutive drives; the infant now strives to restore the damaged object and to make reparation for the harm it feels it has done by its hostile and sadistic impulses."

B. PERVASIVE EFFECTS UPON ATTITUDES AND CHARACTER

(1) Restitution for "undeserved" advantages

Restitution can have wide effects upon character formation and attitudinal development. As such, it not infrequently is seen to be operative along with other mechanisms. The following instance is illustrative. Herein, Restitution, Compensation, and Reaction Formation are all in evidence.

Case 104
Restitution, Compensation, and Reaction Formation

James N. was the first son of the successful and wealthy president of a large manufacturing firm. His family was quite prominent, not only in their own town, but to an extent nationally. He was uneasy from his early years about the special advantages and position which accrued to him and to his family. When Jim was still in high school, he began to secure, entirely on his own, summer jobs which required him to perform the heaviest manual labor in the mills. Here he was very fond of the "earthiness" of the laborers and their families. By his efforts, he came to be considered as "a great guy—one of the boys." He refused his father's offers of employment in the front office.

When he attended college, Jim, a boy of unusual athletic, intellectual, and personality talents, consistently associated with the less privileged groups. Among his best friends were the waiters, janitors, and other "self-helpers" among his classmates. He dated the "towny girls" in preference to the "debs," intelligentsia, and élite at the fashionable New England girls' schools. He spent his time and his money in considerable amounts on his friends among the less privileged students. During his second year at college, Jim entered a "laundry contest" with his two scholarship roommates. He won with ease, having spent $12.00 on laundry for the entire school year.

Strong seeds of Restitution and of Compensation are evident in Jim's behavior and attitudes. Another mechanism operative was the type of Reaction Formation in which he developed attitudes against many of the things with which his father was identified. However, in talks, or spontaneously, Jim would speak with praise and admiration of his father, and stressed the understanding which he and his father shared. His friends fondly nicknamed him "Duke" in slightly jesting deference to his favored position, which in some ways he seemed eager to renounce in a kind of defensive Restitution. They felt more comfortable about his advantages than he did. He felt guilty about them and was far more uncomfortably conscious of differences in status, position, and resources. "Duke," the first son of the majority owner of his own large firm, subsequently entered the profession of law, in which he excelled.

As a final point, it is of interest that disapproved motives, as well as the actions they may lead to, are bases for guilt. Sometimes the guilt is more for the motive, sometimes more for the act, and in varying combinations. Jealousy, for instance, is one emotion of which many disapprove and many do not like to admit, sometimes even to themselves.

(2) Restitution following destructive jealousy

When jealousy leads to a destructive act, this can result in considerable guilt feelings which can in turn require restitutive en-

249

deavors. The following instance is illustrative. Here, also, other mechanisms (Denial, Rationalization, and Repression) were operative.

Case 105
Jealousy, a Destructive Act, and Restitution

A research worker had a good reputation for careful work and was greatly relied upon by the doctor whom he assisted. Still, I was aware of some rumblings from the past about some major mishap in the course of experimental work. During the course of therapy which he subsequently undertook, more about this ultimately came to light.

Some years earlier, he had felt his own career was blocked and he had developed an intense jealousy of the man he worked for. They were nearing the end of a long and complex biochemical project which his chief had originally conceived, and for which he would of course receive the credit. One day in a fit of jealous rage he knocked over a large rack of glass containers of solution and concentrates. The loss resulted in a severe setback time-wise in the research. He ascribed this wanton destruction of the culmination of months of work as accidental.

The chief was furious. He threatened his dismissal, perhaps subconsciously suspecting the deliberateness of the act. The young man himself was aghast at the length to which his jealousy had driven him. However, all of his resulting remorse, self-condemnation, and guilt had not remained conscious. Much had been successfully denied, rationalized, and repressed.

This event, however, had shaken him profoundly. It had led to his becoming a superior researcher as, driven by unconscious needs to assuage his guilt through Restitution, he strove to do his best professionally. This was part of his unconscious endeavor to make up for his act of vandalism and for his consciously intolerable and disowned feelings of envy and jealousy.

4. SUMMARY

Among the major mental mechanisms there is one which is employed in response to superego pressure arising from guilt. Through its employment one unwittingly seeks to make up for, to make reparation for injury or loss which has been inflicted. Evaluation of such harm or hurt is subjective and may or may not be realistic.

I have found it most suitable and a matter of convenience in teaching and communication, to name this important intrapsychic process Restitution.

Restitution is one of the more advanced dynamisms or ego defenses. It has some similarities to Undoing and to Unconscious Atonement and Penance, from which distinctions were also made. Conscious restitution is common and the differences from the unconscious operation of the mental mechanism are not necessarily substantial. The principle of making restitution for wrongdoing, for damages inflicted, for hurt, or for criminal acts, is accepted and is widely prevalent.

(1) Interpersonal Restitution

This form of restitution includes that which is made for real or subjectively assessed wrongs suffered at one's hands by those in close interpersonal situations. They particularly include intrafamilial examples and may influence subsequent behavior from very minor to quite major ways.

(2) Public Restitution

This concept includes that which is demanded by the public, as by process of law, plus that which is voluntarily made to the public. Public Restitution is less stringent today, and any following of the harsh Talion Law as in earlier eras has largely been abandoned.

(3) Social Restitution

In Social Restitution society in general benefits from the restitutive endeavors. Herein, the resulting major changes can approach those in quality resulting from the operation of the mechanism of Sublimation. Occupations may be chosen and one's life work influenced, as illustrated in several clinical examples. The principle of "Never Enough" is widely operative in psychic defenses. In Restitution this term refers to a tendency toward guilt in pitfalls in some restitutive processes, so that both guilty needs and restitutive efforts continue to slowly increase. Restitution is made but it is "never enough." Social Restitution was illustrated through contributions to church and to charity.

(4) Restitution by proxy

This type of Restitution may occur by someone seeking to make Restitution for another. Restitution takes place in dreams. An illustration of the "Dream of Regret" was cited. Many instances of the operation of Restitution in business can be found and several instances were included. Restitution also takes place through bequests, and examples were offered. A short recapitulation of dynamics included two cases in which additional dynamisms were employed.

REFERENCES

1. BRIERLEY, MARJORIE (1951). *Trends in Psycho-Analysis,* p. 60. London; Hogarth.
2. KLEIN, MELANIE (1950). *Developments in Psycho-Analysis,* p. 214. London; Hogarth.
3. *Ibid.,* p. 275.
4. LAUGHLIN, HENRY P. (1956). *The Neuroses in Clinical Practice,* pp. 136–137, 736. Philadelphia; Saunders.
5. *New Yorker,* March, 1958.
6. NOYES, A. P. (1953). *Modern Clinical Psychiatry,* pp. 48, 53. Philadelphia; Saunders.

INDEX